STORIES FROM THE LIFE

OF

JESUS

Adapted by

APRIL OURSLER ARMSTRONG

from

"THE GREATEST STORY EVER TOLD"

by Fulton Oursler

Illustrated by Jules Gotlieb

GARDEN CITY BOOKS

Garden City, N. Y.

Library of Congress Catalog Card Number 55-9510

TO MY FATHER

WITH LOVE

CONTENTS

ONCE before time, this story began, somewhere in the mind and heart of God. It is a story that is not yet ended, a true story in which both you and I must play our parts. It is the story of how God loved the world so much that He sent His own Son to teach us all how to live here on earth so that some day we may all live with Him in heaven.

A long, long time ago, nearly two thousand years as men reckon time, there lived in the town of Nazareth, in the land of Israel, a family especially chosen by God. There was Joachim, the father, a tall man with gray curly hair and smiling cherry-red cheeks. There was Anna, the mother, a gentle hard-working woman with laugh-wrinkles under her eyes. And there was Mary, their daughter, who was nearly sixteen, and wondrously lovely with her intense eyes and her long dark hair.

Nazareth, hidden in the mountains, was on the busy trade route between Europe and Asia, and often long troops of camels came through the streets, carrying bales of silks and spices, and wine and oils, and gold and silver. But Mary and her parents lived in a white house on the edge of town, away from the rowdy bustle of the merchants and the camel-drivers. Joachim tended to his farm and Anna baked the bread and sewed and cared for the house. And Mary helped her mother with the sheep and the chickens, with the cooking and the water-carrying and the washing.

There were three other people who were dear to this

family, three people who were to become very important in the secret plans of God.

One was Joseph, the carpenter. Joseph lived alone behind his carpenter's shop in a high street in the middle of Nazareth. He was a tall man with strong shoulders and a small golden beard, and quiet, thoughtful eyes. He loved Mary, and she loved him, and Joseph hoped the day would come when they would marry, as soon as he had saved enough money.

The other two were Mary's cousin Elizabeth, and Elizabeth's husband, Zachary. Elizabeth had thick wavy white hair. She was the daughter of Anna's much older sister, and she was more than forty years older than the dark-eyed Mary. For Mary, it was like being cousin to your own grandmother! But Mary and Elizabeth were good friends in spite of that.

Cousin Elizabeth was married to a country priest named Zachary, and they lived near his synagogue in a town called Ain Karim, not far from Jerusalem.

Cousin Zachary was even older than Elizabeth. His back was so stiff that he found it hard to stoop over and fasten his sandals. But he was a kind man and good, and in his work in Ain Karim he helped many people to find happiness.

All six of these people—Mary, Joachim, and Anna, Joseph, Elizabeth, and Zachary—loved God. They did their best to serve Him, and they kept His laws, and they prayed to Him each day and night. They were poor people, and plain people. No one outside of their friends had ever heard of them.

But often it is the poorest, the plainest people, whom God loves most. And God had chosen these people to help Him, to play their parts in the story of Jesus—the greatest story ever told.

Mystery in the Temple

ONE brisk day in spring Mary and her mother and father and Joseph left Nazareth, and traveled for three days on donkeys down the long highway to the city of Jerusalem. Travel was difficult in those times, and only a very special occasion could bring them so far away from home.

But this was a special day indeed, for today Cousin Zachary had been chosen for a thrilling honor. This little old country priest was to leave his small town and come to the great Temple in Jerusalem to celebrate the sacrifice to God in that holy place. He would stand before the High Altar in front of thousands of worshipers, and pray for them all. He would wear the yellow and white robes with the blue tassels, and for that day he would be very close to God.

Of course the family came to Jerusalem to share Cousin Zachary's hour of glory. And though Joseph was not yet really part of the family, he was invited to come, too.

11

Joseph and Mary stared with drawn breath at the very size of the Temple, with its roof of blood-red cedar and its marble pillars taller than eight men. The golden rays of sunset swept over the faces of the throngs who waited to take part in the service.

"Ah," sighed Joachim, "there comes Cousin Zachary. Joseph, look! Cousin Elizabeth must have sewn that wonderful robe for him!"

Old Zachary looked almost young as he stood straight and stiff beside the altar. He raised his arms, and closed his eyes—and all the people prayed.

Only Cousin Elizabeth knew that Zachary was praying for a secret wish this afternoon. Only she knew that even though he was over seventy years old he still asked God every day that Elizabeth and he might have a child, for they had never had one.

Zachary turned and faced the people. He held in his right hand a censer of burning incense. The silver plume of smoke was sweet in the evening winds, as he held the censer high and prayed. He walked up the steps beside the altar, lifted the wide curtains, and disappeared from the view of the people. He was in the secret holy place of the Temple, called the tabernacle.

Zachary was supposed to stand in the tabernacle for a moment in silent prayer. He must look at the golden candlesticks in there, and at the cakes of wheat and barley, or the showbread as it was called, and then swing the censer three times in silence. Then he was supposed to back out of the holy place, face the people, and say a final prayer. It should only take a few minutes.

But time passed, and there was no sign of Zachary. The crowd began to rustle, and to wonder if anything was wrong.

"Something is strange," Joachim murmured to Joseph. "Do you think Zachary might be ill?"

Then suddenly Zachary rushed out of the tabernacle, and something very serious was wrong with him. Everyone could see that. He swayed dizzily on the steps, and staggered in front of the altar. His cheeks were pale. His eyes glittered, and his hair was tossed. And he could not make a sound. It was as if he had swallowed the mystery, and therefore could not speak!

The family took Cousin Zachary straight home to his own little house in the village of Ain Karim. They shut the door to keep out all the curious men and women of the town.

Then Zachary sat at the table and in sign language he asked for pen and ink, and a parchment to write on.

"Ah! Ah! For once in his life he gets to the Temple in Jerusalem—and he is stricken dumb! He cannot speak!" Elizabeth sobbed.

But Zachary raised his finger to ask for silence. Slowly, carefully, he wrote his news on the parchment:

"I have been listening to an angel!"

When she read those words, Elizabeth gave a great sigh. Zachary had not only been stricken dumb, she thought, but he had also gone mad.

"That's a terrible thing for a man to say. What an idea —to talk with an angel!"

And Elizabeth walked up and down the little room crying until Zachary got up from the table and stood in her way and stopped her. He had lost his voice, true, but he could still hear. He heard her—and he wanted her to be quiet, and let him write out for her what the angel said!

Cousin Elizabeth's house was a noisy place just at that moment. Everybody except Zachary was talking at once. Anna was trying to comfort Elizabeth, and Joachim was standing in the middle of the floor, trying to get them all to listen to him.

"Since when is a person crazy to believe angels can talk with men? It has happened before—in our own family," said Joachim.

And even Elizabeth remembered that that was true. Joachim's ancestors, his great-great-great-great-great-grandfather, and others of his relatives, had talked with angels. (And we can read all about them today in the part of the Bible we call the Old Testament—about David and Abraham, who were both part of Joachim's family.)

"Why not see what Zachary has to say?" said Joachim.

Zachary smiled in thanks to Joachim. He sank back into his chair. He pointed again to the line he had written:

"I have been listening to an angel."

The others nodded solemnly. Zachary picked up his pen and wrote again:

"I went into the tabernacle, the holy place. A figure was standing there. He stood with folded wings, and looked at me. I was terribly frightened. He spoke in a deep voice, unlike any voice I ever heard. And he said to me: 'Fear not, Zachary, your prayer is heard!' "

Elizabeth's cheeks went white. Over his shoulder she read the angel's words as Zachary wrote them:

" 'Your wife, Elizabeth, shall bear you a son.' "

Elizabeth's eyes opened wide, and she leaned further over Zachary's shoulder. Anna and Mary pressed close beside her as the old man's pen scurried across the page.

" 'And you shall call his name John.' "

"John!" cried Elizabeth. "John! That name means the gracious gift of God!"

Zachary nodded to her. His face was pale as the parchment under his hand. His chin bobbed up and down solemnly. Yes, they were to have a son, and they would call him John.

Anna and Mary and Elizabeth stared at Joachim, and back at Zachary. They scratched their heads. The whole story was hard to believe, yet look at Zachary! He was obviously not play-acting. He had always scorned lies and pretense of any kind. And Zachary had been made dumb. That by itself must mean something. Why was he not permitted to speak?

With shaking hands Zachary asked them to be quiet, and he went on writing. In that same deep unearthly voice, the angel had told Zachary that the boy John would grow up to bring many people to love the Lord their God. More, the angel said that this baby would be like Elias, the famous prophet of the olden days.

"Do you realize what you are writing there?" gasped Elizabeth.

"The coming of a prophet!" murmured Anna. "I told you we are an unusual family. We always were."

"Wait until it happens," replied Elizabeth cautiously. But Zachary was still writing.

"The angel said to me: 'He shall turn the hearts of fathers to their children, and to the unbelieving ones he shall show the wisdom of the just, to prepare a perfect people for the Lord.' "

Zachary looked up at his wife and shrugged.

"Then I felt a little better," he wrote, "because I recognized those words. They come from one of our holy books, the Book of Malachi, the last of our prophets. And so because I knew the words I felt a little more at ease, more like myself. And so I am afraid I was a little rude and disrespectful to the angel. At least, I got up my courage to speak for the first time and asked him a question. I simply asked him: 'How shall I know that I will have a son? For I am an old man, and my wife too is very old.' "

"And what did he say to that, Zachary?" asked Elizabeth.

"He answered me at once," wrote Zachary. "He simply said that he was Gabriel."

Gabriel! Gabriel was an archangel—they all knew that.

"He told me that God had sent him to the Temple to tell me this glorious news. But he seemed much more serious now, let me tell you. And then he told me I was not going to be allowed to talk—until the day when these things came to pass. And he said that was a punishment, because I had not believed his words."

Zachary dropped his pen and pointed to his open mouth. He grew red in the face from trying, but he could not make a sound. Not even a groan.

Elizabeth insisted on calling the town doctor to look at her husband. The doctor hemmed and hawed and grunted. Then he ordered Zachary to eat only warm barley soup and figs, and to lie flat on his back for three days. Of course, no one told him the story of the angel. That was a family secret, right or wrong.

Soon after the doctor left, Zachary fell into a deep sleep. The others stayed up late into the night talking. Elizabeth found it hard to believe that Zachary was anything but sick. Anna was puzzled. Joachim firmly and stubbornly believed everything the old man had said.

Joseph kept silent. And no one asked Mary what she thought. She was not yet more than sixteen, and in her parents' eyes she was still a child. But before they went to bed, Mary said to Elizabeth:

"Cousin dear, you have prayed a long time for a child. I believe in your prayers, Elizabeth. Why should we be surprised if God has heard them and will answer them? Why not wait—and believe?"

And that, as time was soon to prove, was the wisest thing said in the family that night.

The next morning there was not much talk about the mystery of Zachary and the angel.

At breakfast Joachim and Anna talked about the weather and the farm and the taxes, exactly as if nothing had happened. And Joachim decided they must be starting home that afternoon.

People talk a great deal about the little excitements of their lives—the giant fish they have caught, the mighty storms or beasts they have defeated. They talk even more about the big things that have not happened, of tall tales and dreams. But when something tremendous does happen, something they cannot explain or understand—*a miracle*—they say little.

Even on the return journey they spoke only once or twice about Zachary and the angel. They did not really want to think about it because it was all so strange and so frightening.

Back in Nazareth the months passed swiftly and the mystery of the Temple was almost forgotten until one night a letter arrived at the house of Anna and Joachim and young Mary.

The letter came from Elizabeth and Zachary. It began with the usual greeting that people used in those days: "Peace be with you."

"Peace be with you," Elizabeth had written. "God has heard our prayers indeed. And the angel's words are coming true. Anna, my darling aunt, listen, and tell Joachim and dear Mary and that fine young man Joseph—listen—though I am an old, old woman, I am really going to have a child!"

What a night of excitement that was! Everyone was talking at once about Elizabeth and the baby she would soon have, the baby the angel had said must be called John.

And in their hearts they marveled at the mysterious ways of God, whose will is done on earth as it is in heaven, even when men and women do not understand the reason or the way in which it is done. From that day on they would find it easier to believe in miracles and mysteries of God. And for this family there were many more miracles to come.

Mary and the Angel

IT was spring in Nazareth. Joseph the carpenter closed the door on the clean smell of sawdust and shavings in his shop and walked through the village with a smile on his face. In the sunset the green hillsides glowed with little yellow and crimson anemones. You could even taste the flower sweetness in the wind.

Everywhere around him were noisy happy people, each hurrying about his own business in the twilight. Now and then one of Joseph's customers hailed him—a farmer for whom he had made a plow, a man for whom he had made a table and six benches. Then Joseph turned into a lane, away from the crowds. He was going to the house where Mary lived with Joachim, her father, and Anna, her mother. He had a surprise for all of them.

Ahead of him loomed the white dome of their house. At one side of it a staircase ran to the roof, and looking up there Joseph saw Mary, the beautiful dark-eyed, black-haired girl Joseph loved. She had a lantern in her hand and she was bending over, collecting dates and figs that had been spread out to dry in the hot sun that day. She heard Joseph's footsteps and she straightened up and waved her hand.

Inside the house Anna, like most wives of the village, was busy over a pot of burning coals, preparing to bake fresh loaves of bread. Joachim rose to greet Joseph with a bow, and a smile of welcome.

Joseph seated himself beside the older man. "I have

come to ask you if I may marry your daughter, Mary," he said. "I have saved the money I have earned with my hammer and saw. I am ready now to buy all the things we need— a goat, and hens and a rooster. And I love Mary heart and soul. Have I your permission to speak to Mary?"

Joachim nodded solemnly.

Anna looked over her shoulder as she patted the dough into loaves. "I know that you love Mary, and that she loves you. There is no reason to wait," she said. "You may ask Mary."

After supper that night Joseph and Mary walked alone through the damp darkness of the lane, and made their plans. Together under the golden new moon, and the hushed stars, they set the day for their wedding. Within three months they would be married. The night winds smelled of clover and new grass, a night they thought had been specially made to celebrate their happiness.

"This is an evening I shall never forget," said Joseph, as he took Mary's hand to say goodbye.

"Nor will I, Joseph," said Mary, as she watched him turn down the lane back to his carpenter's shop to sleep.

But neither Mary nor Joseph could guess how unforgettable this night would be, nor the tremendous secret that still lay hidden in the shining stars above.

Mary stood at the gate alone for a moment dreaming. Her mother and father had been sitting up on the roof, talking quietly. The hens and roosters were fast asleep on their perches. The dog was barking behind the garden, and the sheep and goats were dozing.

An ordinary night—*hardly a setting for a miracle!*

Mary smiled and started into the house, her pale blue mantle floating behind her in the breeze. She was expecting nothing more exciting than a good night's sleep. She crossed the lower floor inside the house, and climbed to the inner terrace.

As she went up the steps she realized she was not alone. A tall stranger was standing near the farther wall!

He seemed to stand in light—but there was no lamp there. A kind of silvery mist lay around him, as if the light were his cap and gown. Mary opened her mouth to speak, to ask who he was and what he wanted, but he spoke first.

"Hail, Mary!"

The voice was kind, and deep as the ocean. Mary had never heard a voice like it before, deep and manly, and yet gentle.

"Full of grace!" the voice continued.

Hail, Mary, full of grace! Mary felt shy, and even a little frightened, to have someone speak to her like this.

"The Lord is with you. Blessed are you among women."

Mary folded her hands, and she saw that her hands were shaking, and her arms, and even her shoulders. The stranger also saw she was trembling.

"Do not be afraid, Mary."

She bowed her head. She must not be afraid. She knew she could trust this deep and tender voice. But she could not stop trembling. She closed her eyes and listened to what the stranger was saying. He was telling her that God was greatly pleased with her, and that God was going to give her a baby —a son.

"And you shall call His name Jesus!" said the stranger.

Little thoughts like wild birds darted through Mary's mind. She thought: "Jesus! He will be my son, Jesus. Jesus, son of Mary! I shall have a baby boy, and hold Him in my arms, and sometimes I shall give Him to Joseph to hold, too!"

Yet Mary must listen to the stranger. He was telling her more wonderful things about her son Jesus. He said that Jesus was to have a throne, the throne of the famed king of Israel, King David of history.

"And of all His kingdom, there shall be no end."

Mary listened closely, but still she had not understood the amazing truth that the stranger was trying to tell her. She did not even know who the stranger was, but one question she had to ask him.

"How shall this be done?" she asked in a whisper. "For I am not married."

The stranger stepped nearer and she saw his folded wings, and then she knew him for what he really was, an angel. In the starry fire of his eyes she saw not a frown, but gentle warmth.

His voice grew lower and deeper still:

"The Holy Ghost shall come upon you. The power of the Most High shall overshadow you, and the Holy Child which shall be born of you shall be called—the Son of God."

Mary felt as if she could not breathe, as she heard those words. She would be the mother of a son who would be called the Son of God?

How could one little Nazareth girl take all that in?

The voice of the angel whispered:

"Your cousin Elizabeth . . ."

Mary nodded. She remembered well the day when an angel had told Cousin Elizabeth and Cousin Zachary that they were to have a baby, even though they were old, very old. And indeed what that angel had said came true, for a letter had come from Elizabeth, announcing that she was to have a child.

The angel went on reminding Mary:

"Elizabeth is also to have a son, and she is in her old age! In three months she who never had a child will have a son. Because with God nothing shall be impossible!"

Nothing shall be impossible! Not even for Mary, the girl of sixteen, the girl who tends her father's animals and helps her mother with the baking and the sewing, to have a child who will be the Son of God.

For one instant Mary knew that if she agreed to what

the angel said, she would know great sorrow, and pain in the life ahead of her. Things would never again be the same. It was not an easy thing the angel was asking, and Mary knew it, even though she could not then understand all it would mean.

She did not hesitate. She looked up at him, her eyes half closed, her words so soft she could barely hear herself speak.

"Behold, I shall be the handmaid of the Lord. Let it all happen to me, as you have said."

The angel vanished. One instant he was there, gone the next.

Mary crossed the floor and went down on her knees, and then lay on her cot and closed her eyes and wept, and prayed.

Too much for her to understand! She wanted to call out to her mother, to throw herself in her mother's strong arms, and tell her what had happened. But she could not bring herself to tell her secret, just then. They would never believe her. Anna, her mother, and Joachim, her father, still thought of her as a child, anyway.

They would say she had imagined this thing because Cousin Elizabeth was having a child, and Cousin Zachary had said he saw an angel.

Mary lay there quietly while Anna and Joachim tiptoed down from the roof. They went to sleep after their prayers. But Mary could not sleep. She slipped out of bed two hours later. She wrote her mother a note, made herself a bundle of some fresh clothes and a little bread and cheese to eat. She set off alone down the long road.

There was one other person in the world whom she felt she must tell first about her meeting with the angel.

She was walking to Cousin Elizabeth. And as Mary had known, Elizabeth understood the wonderful thing that had happened, and believed it.

Mary stayed with her cousin until Elizabeth's baby was born, the child the angel had said would be called John, the child who grew to be the man we know today as John the Baptist. And as the angel had said, Cousin Zachary who had not been able to speak for nearly a year, found his voice when the baby was born.

"Blessed be the Lord God of Israel!" said Zachary, as he held his son in his arms.

Then Mary went home, and told her mother and her father of the angel who had spoken to her. She told them that she was to have a Son, a baby who would be called Jesus, who would be the Son of God.

And though Mary was afraid they would laugh at her, and tell her she was dreaming, they believed her, for God had whispered in their hearts and told them. And because Anna and Joachim loved her, and Joseph too, they could understand, for that is the way things always are with those who love each other, and love God.

The First Christmas

IN the marble throne room of the palace in Rome, an emperor grinned. His treasury was nearly empty, and he needed more money to spend on his golden chariots and perfumed fountains, on his legions of soldiers and his thousands of slaves. Again and again he had taxed the people of the whole Roman Empire for more gold to be spent on statues of himself, or on gladiators and wild lions for the games in the arena. Still he needed more money. For weeks he had worried and fumed over a way to fill his treasury.

Then suddenly the fat old Emperor Caesar Augustus smiled, and the smile widened to a grin. He had found the answer. He would take a census of his whole empire, count every man, woman, and child in the biggest cities and the smallest towns. Then he would know from whom he could take more money. It was a clever idea, and it made him very happy.

Far away from Rome lay one of his colonies, conquered Palestine, homeland of the Jews. Already Palestine was paying money to Rome. Every man had to give a tenth of his corn to the government, and two-tenths of his grapes and fruit, too. And then there was the poll tax, one per cent from everybody. And all the other taxes.

But now there were to be even more taxes.

Emperor Caesar Augustus sent a letter to his friend Cyrenus, who was the governor of Syria, and was in charge of Palestine too. The Emperor ordered Cyrenus to take a census of everyone living in Palestine, to count every Jew in the country so that no one could escape paying the new tax, and the Emperor's money vaults would again glitter with gold.

And in Palestine word of the new census spread through every street in the little town of Nazareth—and no one in Nazareth liked the idea at all. They had an ancient, proud dislike of being counted. And they had a very modern, very sensible dislike of paying taxes for the Emperor to waste on foolishness.

Joseph the carpenter, and Mary his bride, heard the news most unhappily in their little home behind the carpenter shop. Any day now, Mary was to have her Baby, the Child promised by the angel, the boy the angel called the Son of God. Mary and Joseph had hoped the Baby would be born at home. They certainly did not want to take a long trip just before He came!

But Cyrenus the governor had his own notions of how to take a census. He had sent out orders to every village explaining that to be sure everybody was counted, each person must pack up and go to the city of the tribe to which he belonged. Now Joseph belonged to the tribe of King David, and so he must go all the way down to Bethlehem to be counted.

"Not only you," Joseph was told. "Your wife must also go to her rightful headquarters to be counted."

"How can Mary go?" he protested. "Don't you know she is going to have a Baby any day?"

But the orders were firm. They must leave at once to be in Bethlehem on the day of the census!

Later Joseph talked with Mary about it. He reminded Mary how long ago Moses had separated the men of Israel into tribes, or houses as they were also called. And ever since families had kept careful records of the tribe to which they belonged. The scrolls of writing in the Nazareth synagogue made it clear that both Joseph and Mary must go to Bethlehem because that was David's city, and they were both of the house of David.

"Why—oh, why—must there be a census—or a trip to Bethlehem?" said Joseph unhappily.

But Mary smiled. "Joseph, my beloved," she said, "remember what the angel said to me?"

"He said, 'Do not be afraid, Mary!' "

"Then," said Mary, "we should not be afraid. And there is something else. I have been listening to the Scriptures in the synagogue, and there are prophecies, Joseph."

"Prophecies about the Messiah, the Savior, the Son of God?"

"Yes. The prophets have said that when the Son of God comes, He will be born in Bethlehem. Had you forgotten, Joseph?"

Joseph gasped.

"Mary, my beloved, we shall go to Bethlehem."

The next morning they began their journey.

From Nazareth it is seventy-five miles to Bethlehem of Judea. Joseph and Mary were not going alone. Mary's mother and father, the kind, strong Anna and Joachim, also had to go and be counted. The two women, Anna and Mary, rode on stubborn little donkeys, while the men trudged alongside and held onto the reins. But donkeys go slowly, and the journey would take them more than three days.

The road was crowded with other families on donkey and on foot. Thousands of people cluttered the highway, all leaving their homes to go and be counted because the Emperor of Rome had said they must. Though they did not like having to go, most of them made a holiday out of the trip. They camped and cooked by the side of the road, and at night pitched tents around wood fires. They slept on blankets spread upon the ground.

During the day they sang their favorite songs, the ones you will find in your Bible called the Psalms of David. Several men had brought along little harps and plucked at the strings, making music as they marched. So it was not a lonely journey and Mary and Joseph were not unhappy.

A shout went up.

"Bethlehem!"

At last they were there, and at last, they thought, they could rest from the long, dusty trip. Joseph took Mary's hand and they looked together at the golden light of a winter sunset slanting on the white houses, and on the hillsides where flocks of sheep were grazing drowsily. This was Bethlehem, where the Son of God was to be born. They looked at each other with silent happiness over their secret.

But as they entered the streets of Bethlehem, Joseph's face wrinkled with worry above his golden beard. The crowds were so great! You could hardly move through the streets because from all over the country the men and women and children of the tribe of David had come to this town to be counted.

Joseph knew he must find a room for Mary at once. The sun was already going, and the night would be cold.

Joseph asked everyone he met to show him the way to an inn, but no one listened. One boy even laughed in his face at such a question.

"Don't you know there are no rooms left in Bethlehem, not even a bed?" taunted the boy as he ran away into the crowd.

Joseph did find five different inns, but they were all filled. He could not understand why no one seemed to care about Mary. He could not understand why there should be no room anywhere for the baby who was coming, the baby who was the Son of God. Even today men and women and children are sometimes so busy thinking of themselves that they cannot make room for the Baby Jesus, even in their hearts.

But Joseph kept on looking. He would not give up. He had to find a room for Mary. At last he found the sixth and last inn in Bethlehem. He shouldered his way through the crowd at the door.

"My wife is about to have a baby," he pleaded. "I must have a bed for her at least."

The innkeeper was a stout and grumpy man with an enormous stomach. He had rolls of fat under his chin, and little dumplings of fat under his eyes, and oily gray curls.

"There is no room," he said. Then he clasped his red hands in front of him and stared at Joseph, at Mary, at Anna and Joachim. Something about them made him stop and think. For a moment he said nothing, then he curled fat fingers around his mouth and bawled:

"Sarah!"

His wife, just as fat as he, came shuffling from the back of the inn.

"What do you want?" She growled at Mary and Joseph. "Don't you realize the town is full? There is not a bed in the town tonight. Still . . ."

The greasy woman turned to her husband.

"There is one place we haven't put anybody yet."

"Is there now? Where? Just where?" demanded the innkeeper.

Joseph smiled with hope. Perhaps there was a nice, warm, comfortable room waiting for Mary. . . .

"No one's in the stable," said the woman.

"The stable!" said Joseph miserably.

But Mary smiled at the innkeeper's wife. "Thank you," said Mary. "A stable is warm. And it will be a little like home, because often I used to sleep downstairs with the sheep and the goats."

The stable was in a roomy cave under the inn. Joseph held Mary's hand as he led her down twisting stone steps to the floor of earth. The lantern he carried threw strange twisting shadows against the rough walls. As Anna helped Mary to make herself comfortable, Joseph stood apart with Joachim, and wondered.

"I always thought that when Jesus was born, He would come in a great cloud of glory and excitement, with everything beautiful around Him. After all, He is God, and King of all. Yet here we are, in a stable, with only donkeys and cows and a dirt floor."

Then suddenly, Joseph and Joachim heard a small clear voice in the stable—a child's first cry.

The Baby was born.

Joseph knelt beside Mary's bed of straw.

"See!" whispered Mary, as she held the Baby. Her Son was wrapped in grandmother Anna's handmade swaddling clothes, the long strips of linen in which all babies then were wrapped.

"Jesus is born!"

The Baby's face was smooth and radiant, and filled with innocence and love. This was the Son of God, whom the angel had said would be born to Mary. This was the Savior of the world, the Messiah, whom prophets had promised would come to redeem the world.

And so it was that because an emperor in Rome was greedy for more taxes, the baby Jesus was born not at home, but in Bethlehem as the ancient holy men had foretold. And because there was no room at the inn, the Child who was the King of Heaven, the Prince of Peace, was born in the poorest place on earth—a stable.

Mary laid Him in a manger, the food box of the donkeys and the cows, which Joseph had cleaned and filled with fresh straw.

The donkeys brayed, and the sheep were bleating, and the warm deep breaths of the cows filled the cave. The stable smelled sweet with the fresh odors of barley and oats and hay. And though it was not the fine palace which Joseph would have liked to offer God as a home, the stable was beautiful on that first Christmas. God had blessed it, and His Son was there.

Shepherds at the Back Door

IN the crisp darkness of the first Christmas the stable in Bethlehem was silent.

Mary had fallen asleep, wrapped in her long blue mantle. Anna, her mother, and Joachim, her father, had made a bed for themselves far back in the shadows, near the warm breath of the oxen and the sheep. And Jesus, the Baby, lay asleep in His first bed, the manger filled with fresh hay and barley smelling so sweet and clean.

Only Joseph was awake. He could not sleep. He walked quietly around the stable, around and around, stopping regularly to look down at Mary and her Child. Excitement shivered through him, and happiness, and only one thing saddened him, that he had no one to talk to in that dark hour. And so, because he had no one near, he talked to himself, about the wonder of Christmas.

"The odd thing is," he told himself, "that when I looked into that Baby's eyes, I seemed to have known Him all my life. You don't feel that way with most babies. But He—He wasn't a stranger!"

Then Joseph stopped for a minute in his walking.

"One thing," he said to himself, "puzzles me. This Baby is Jesus, the Son of God. The angel told Mary that a long time ago in Nazareth. And yet—we have seen no angels since. There's been nothing but plain ordinary everyday things. Wouldn't you think that when He was born something special would happen? Here's the Baby. Where are the angels?"

Joseph listened, hoping to catch the rustle of an angel's wings, but all he heard was the sleepy bleat of a yearling lamb. And then presently he heard a low rumble of voices in the distance, and the shuffling of feet outside. Then came a knocking at the back stable door.

Joseph hurried to the door, afraid that the knocking would waken Mary. Lifting the latch, he opened the upper half of the door, then put a finger warningly to his mouth. Outside a group of men with bearded faces stared in at him. One man held up a lighted lantern. Behind them the night sky was ablaze with the sparkle of stars, brighter than Joseph ever remembered seeing.

"Peace!" whispered Joseph. "This is no time to make noise."

"The Lord be with you," said one of the men gently. "We have not come to make any trouble at all."

"Who are you then?"

"We are shepherds from the hills outside this town. We have been watching our flocks of sheep."

"The hour is late," said Joseph. He started to close the

door on them, but the shepherd who had spoken held up his staff.

"Wait. Only one question we must ask you. Has a Child just been born in this place?"

Joseph drew in his breath, alarmed. Was something wrong, he wondered? Perhaps they had broken a law in sheltering in a stable? No one ever knew what queer laws there might be in these days, between the fat old Emperor in Rome and the ugly King Herod in Jerusalem.

Carefully, Joseph said, "Why do you ask, shepherd? Why is it your business to know if a Child is born here?"

"Don't be afraid of us, man," said the shepherd. "We are friends."

"Well, then," said Joseph. "Yes. A Child has been born here."

"Only a little while ago?" asked the shepherd.

"Yes. In the last two hours."

All the bearded shepherds turned and looked at each other with excitement, and one of them whispered:

"It is true, then."

The shepherd who had spoken before laid a hand on Joseph's shoulder. "Tell me—is it a Boy that is born?"

"It is."

"And tell me, did you put the Baby to sleep in a manger?"

"Yes," answered Joseph. "There was no cradle, you see. The town is so crowded, and there was nowhere else I could take my lady except to this poor stable . . ."

"Then God be praised!" murmured the shepherd, and the others nodded.

"Listen, man," said the one with the lantern. "We five men have just seen a marvelous sight. An unbelievable thing. And it has to do with you!"

"Listen to us," said another. "We were all out on the hillsides tonight, watching over our sheep, minding our own business. The night was clear, air cool, stars bright, every-thing going along just as usual. We were sitting talking, when suddenly Jonas here interrupted us, and pointed at the sky."

"That I did," said Jonas. "There was a great big bright light in the sky, and it was shaped like an angel bigger than the world. And I heard a voice . . ."

"We all saw the light," declared the first man. "And we all heard the voice from the sky."

"What did the voice say?" asked Joseph eagerly.

"It told us not to be afraid."

"Yes," said Joseph, "the angels always say that first. And then?"

"And then it said it brought us great news. The Savior of the world was being born. I remember the words. How can I ever forget them? The angel said, 'For this day is born to you a Savior who is Christ the Lord.' "

"Christ the Lord," whispered Joseph.

"Yes, friend. That's what the voice said. It told us the Child was being born right here in this town and that we would find Him wrapped in swaddling clothes and lying in a manger."

Another shepherd pushed himself forward.

"You can never imagine what happened then," he broke in excitedly. "The whole heaven seemed to open up. The curtain of stars in the sky flew open, and we saw a host of angels that filled the sky, and they were all singing at the top of their voices . . ."

"And do you know what they were singing?" asked Jonas. "They sang: 'Glory to God in the highest and on earth peace . . .' "

And then the shepherds seemed to lose their tongues. The sound of their own story seemed to quiet them. They were strong, out-of-doors men, not the kind who usually talk of babies and God and of angels in the skies. Suddenly they felt that they must seem foolish.

"Of course," said their leader. "We can't expect you to believe all this."

Then his eyes flashed open, and he looked straight at Joseph. "But it is true," he said. "I saw it. I heard it."

Joseph took his hand. "I believe you," he said.

Then they hurried to tell him how they had left their fat-tailed sheep and run into Bethlehem. Of everyone left on the streets in that midnight hour they had asked questions: Where could they find the new-born Baby? And someone had sent them to the stable of the inn.

The shepherds' tale warmed Joseph's heart. He had been looking for an angel to come to him, some sign that the Son of God was born. But the sign had come to others, which was better. These men, panting and out of breath and sweaty, strong and humble, had seen the gates of heaven open. They had heard singing from on high, the heavens rejoicing at the birth of Mary's Child. Plain, poor working men of the fields were the first to come and visit the new-born Jesus.

Joseph threw back the door to let them in, and received them with open arms. One by one on tiptoe the shepherds followed him and he led them straight to the manger. They looked down and then knelt beside the sleeping Jesus.

Soon they were gone, back to their sheep on the hillsides. Joseph, still wakeful, kept watch over Mary and the Child. In his mind's ear he could hear the countless hosts of heaven singing a message not only for the shepherds, but for all who were ever to live in God's world:

"Peace on earth to men of good will."

"Two Pigeons, Please!"

HOW do you bring up a baby who is the Son of God?" That was the one question that bothered Joseph and Mary most of all. When other mothers and fathers have children they know that there are rules the children must obey. But Jesus was not an ordinary child by any means, because He was the Savior of the world, and He was God.

"Should we make Him obey the same rules as everyone else?" Joseph wondered. "It is a strange thing to be the foster father of the Son of God, to have Him helpless in your arms, and watch over Him as if He were just an ordinary child."

Joseph and Mary had to decide quickly what they were going to do, because in the times they lived there were many rules about babies. Joseph and Mary were part of the Jewish faith, because of course there were no Christians then at all. They were good Jews, and they followed all the laws of the Temple.

One law said that when a family had its first boy-baby the mother and father must bring him to the Temple when he was exactly forty days old. The law said that the first son of each family should be offered to God, as a sign that the family loved and honored the Lord. And the family should buy either a lamb or a pigeon as an offering in the Temple.

"He is my first-born Son," said Mary. "And He should be taken to the Temple, and offered to God."

"But He *is* God," said Joseph. "Can such a law be meant for Him?"

"We obey the rules, Joseph."

Joseph smiled. "Yes. God made the laws to show us how to live. We did not make the laws and so we cannot change them. Our job is to try to understand them, and obey them. God knows what is best. And while we care for His Son, we must follow His laws."

And so it was that when the Baby was forty days old, the little family set out for Jerusalem. Jesus and Mary and Joseph and Anna and Joachim left the stable under the inn and rode on donkeys up the road to Jerusalem. The air was crisp and wintry, but the sun was bright, and the world looked beautiful to the mother with her Child in her arms.

The road led up through steep cliffs and ravines, and bleak brown hills. Jerusalem was on a high crest, and it shone in the sunlight like gold. The wall of the city was the color of a yellow cat, and it was made of tawny stones piled thirty feet high. In the wall were eight gates, and sixty watch towers guarded by the cruel soldiers of King Herod. But the baby Jesus and His family went in through the gate called the Sheep's Gate, and no soldier even turned to look at them, they seemed so poor and unimportant.

At the outer gate of the Temple, Cousin Zachary and Cousin Elizabeth with baby John in her arms met them with happy smiles. They had come to help celebrate this day when the Child would be presented in the Temple.

They all went into the Temple together, and stopped to buy the sacrifice they would offer to God. Rich people would buy a one-year-old lamb to offer God, but Joseph's money-pouch was far from full, and so he decided to buy two young pigeons instead. He picked out one and Mary the other, and Joseph carried them in his hands as they went on into the wide Temple court.

Mary was walking a few steps behind Joseph, holding

the sleeping Jesus in her arms. Suddenly a dark, lean shadow fell across the face of the mother and Child. From behind a long line of marble pillars an old man tottered into their path. Mary stopped still.

"What does he want?" whispered Anna.

But Cousin Zachary, the priest, who knew his way about the Temple, smiled calmly, and whispered back:

"Do not be afraid. His name is Simeon. Everyone around the Temple knows old Simeon. He will not hurt you."

Anna still looked frightened of the old man, who was slowly coming nearer and nearer to them.

"He is a good man," said Zachary, "who loves God. He tells everybody that he once had a special vision. An angel promised him that before he died he would see the Savior."

Old Simeon, tall and ragged, came closer and closer toward Mary and Joseph and the Child. The others stopped, and drew back to watch. There was a moment of curious silence as Simeon stared at the Baby in Mary's arms.

Then swiftly, violently, the old man raised his arms to heaven and tears ran down his cheeks.

"At last!" he cried. "At last! I have seen the Messiah!" And in his strange, gnarled voice he thanked God.

From all over the Temple people heard him, and gathered round. They all knew the story of Simeon's visit from the angel. They knew that he had waited in the Temple for years and years, hoping for a sight of the Savior. In silence they watched him now. He leaned forward, his face with its thousand wrinkles close to Mary.

"This Child will be the downfall of many people," he gasped, "but to many He will bring new life. He is set for the fall and for the resurrection of many in Israel."

He raised his bony right hand, and with his thin twisted finger he pointed crookedly at Mary's heart.

"A sword shall pierce your soul!" said Simeon huskily. "Out of many hearts thoughts shall be revealed."

And then, before anyone could speak, there came a new voice—the voice of an old, wizened, wrinkled woman, who stepped from the shadows like a spirit of the past.

"Her name is Anna, like yours," said Zachary to Mary's mother. "She is unbelievably old, even older than Simeon. For eighty-four years she has been a widow. She has been in the Temple since the day it was built, and she never leaves. Night and day she prays to God."

Anna stood in front of Mary, and looked down into the face of the sleeping Child.

"Here, indeed, is the deliverer of the people!" she cried. "Here is the Messiah—the Savior!"

The crowd stared at Mary and her Child, and at Anna and Simeon. And then they all turned and walked away, shaking their heads.

"Poor old Simeon," they said, "he is so old he has lost his mind. And Anna too. Imagine thinking that tiny Baby from the country could be the Savior!"

"Why, they're just plain ordinary people—too poor to buy a lamb. See they have only pigeons to offer. That couldn't be the Son of God!"

And so Mary and Joseph offered their pigeons, and Mary offered her Son to God in the Temple, and went back again to Bethlehem, and no one—except old Anna and old Simeon—noticed them at all.

The Temple was full of people that day who had come there especially to pray to God, and yet they did not see Him when He was there in person, in Mary's arms. They did not know that God can be found sometimes in the smallest things. And they did not believe that God Himself could ever be born as a baby, just to save the world.

Four Kings and a Child

IN a vast ivory and gold palace on a high hill in Jerusalem lived a king whose name was Herod. Herod was ruler of all Palestine, but no one in the whole land liked him, for his heart was twisted and cruel, and when he grew angry the roar of his voice and the stamping of his boots could be heard far outside the castle walls.

Herod had everything that gold and silver could buy. He had his own musicians and dancing girls and slaves to bring him rare fruits and wine, and to fan him with palm leaves. He had perfumed fountains and a silken couch, and strong white horses, and crowns of rubies. But Herod was never happy. And on this winter day his face scowled darker than the gray-clouded sky.

For weeks he had been hearing strange stories about some special Baby who had been born in Palestine, and the stories worried him. He had heard that some shepherds had seen angels in the sky, and that a holy old man, and an old woman too, had cried out in the Temple that a Baby had been born who would be a Savior for the people.

"What kind of dangerous talk is this? What do they mean, a Savior?" said Herod to himself. "Maybe they mean to make this Baby a king! But I am the King! I can't have such talk going on!"

And so Herod called his soldiers and his spies and told them to try to find this Baby, and learn more about Him. If there really were such a Child called the Prince of Peace, then Herod, the angry king, would destroy Him!

The next day his spies came back with alarming news.

"Three strangers have come to Jerusalem from the East. People say they are kings in disguise. They ride camels, and men call them magi."

"What are magi?" asked Herod.

"Magi are wise men," was the answer. "But these three go around asking questions as if they were not very wise."

"What questions?" growled Herod.

"They are asking about a Child who has just been born —a Child they say will some day be King of Israel. They say they have seen His star in the east and have come to kneel before Him."

"A Child who will be King?" Herod's dark face grew purple with anger, as he stormed up and down the room. "I must find this Child myself—and get rid of Him. He could be very dangerous!"

Suddenly Herod stood still. "Perhaps these wise men can tell me where He is. I shall speak to them, and pretend that I, too, want to kneel before this fabulous Child. Bring them here!"

Before they came, Herod dressed himself in his most kingly robes. He put on his crown of diamonds and rubies, with the tall tuft of rainbow-colored feathers. And then he welcomed them to his throne room.

The three wise men bowed to Herod, and announced their names—Caspar, Melchior, and Balthazar. Tall, keen-eyed they were, these Magi, and one, Herod noted, was black in color, a man from Nubia.

Herod smiled exactly as if nothing at all worried him. "What has brought such great people as you to Palestine?"

"We are following a star," said Caspar, the dark-skinned.

"A star?" repeated Herod. "Then you have seen a star our learned men have not found."

The wise men said nothing.

"Well, at any rate," said Herod, "what do you say this star means?"

The Wise Men were very wise, indeed, because they merely shook their heads, and said they could not tell.

"We simply follow the star."

"But," persisted Herod, "what do you expect to find under this star?"

"A Child," said Balthazar, closing his eyes.

"A Child?" Herod's voice was creamy with interest. "And what about this Child?"

"We cannot say till we find Him," said Melchior.

"Very well, then," growled Herod. "Where do you expect to find Him?"

"Bethlehem!"

"Bethlehem. But it is only a small country place!"

The Wise Men shrugged. "We can only follow the star. Tonight we will go on, following it. Where it leads us, we go."

Then Herod had an idea to trap the Wise Men. "Go and find the Child," he said, "and then come back and tell me and I will go and worship Him too."

Herod sent his spies to follow the Wise Men, and find the Child that was born under a magical star. But in the darkness of that night Caspar, Melchior, and Balthazar went by a secret lane to Bethlehem, and the king's spies could not find them to follow them.

The Wise Men found the town and the inn, and the star led them straight to the stable. They knelt beside the manger, and their eyes were full of love and glory as they gazed upon Mary's baby, Jesus the Son of God.

And then Caspar and Melchior and Balthazar each left a gift by the manger, and bowing, they went out again into the night. Because it was late they went to another inn to sleep, and they planned to go the next day to tell King Herod they had found the Baby. But while they slept they dreamed,

all of them the same dream, warning them not to go to Herod, but to go straight away to their own country by a different road. Because of that dream they rose in the middle of the night and mounted their camels and rode away. Herod would never learn from them where Jesus was!

That same night Joseph had a dream, even more strange. An angel came to him and said:

"Get up and take the Child and His mother and go quickly into Egypt, and stay there until I tell you. Because Herod is looking for the Child, hoping to kill Him!"

Joseph leaped from his bed, at once. But how could they go to Egypt? It was many weeks' journey to Egypt. They would need money to travel so far, and he had only a few coins left, because for weeks now he had been away from his work as a carpenter.

What to do?

Through the darkness he saw Joachim, his father-in-law, coming toward him.

"Joseph, I could not sleep. And so I unpacked the gifts the Wise Men left for the Child. Do you know what they brought?"

Joseph shook his head. "I am too worried now, Joachim."

"Look," said Joachim. "Here is frankincense—the most perfect perfume of all. And myrrh, the fragrant spice. And here—here is gold!"

"Gold?" Joseph leaned closer to see. "Joachim, it is as if God knew we would need it, and sent it to us, just so we could do what His angel said! Gold for our trip. Listen, Joachim——" And Joseph told the older man of his dream.

In the blackness of night Joseph woke Mary. They said fond goodbyes to Anna and Joachim. Then Joseph put Mary and her Baby on the donkey's back, and tied the bundles of their clothes and goods to the saddle. Staff in one hand, Joseph took the donkey reins with the other, and in the middle of the dark the family started out from Bethlehem. They were taking the road to Egypt.

When King Herod heard that the Wise Men had disappeared without telling him where the Baby was, he screamed with anger.

"I will find that Child—no matter what I must do. I must get rid of Him, that upstart Babe with His angels and His stars!"

And then a horrible idea came to Herod, an idea so terrifying that even he grew pale at the thought. He knew the Child was supposed to be in Bethlehem. And the idea came to this cruel monster of a king that if he killed all the babies in Bethlehem he would be safe from the Child who was the Prince of Peace.

Herod's soldiers went to Bethlehem with swords and spears, and by his orders they killed every boy baby in town. Not one of those holy innocents was spared.

But Herod could not hurt the infant Jesus.

For God had warned Joseph, and Joseph had done just as the angel had said. The holy family was safely on the long road into Egypt.

The Boy Who Knew

EGYPT, miles across the lonely desert from Palestine, was a land of mystery and of strange gods, the last place on earth one would look to find the Baby Jesus. Yet King Herod's spies did seek Him even there.

"Has anyone seen a bald-headed carpenter from Nazareth, with a dark-eyed wife, and an Infant?" they asked the white-robed men of the desert.

"Have you seen a Baby that is somehow different from all others?" they asked the dark-eyed men in the shadows of the pyramids. "A Baby with a smile like the warm light of the sun?"

Even after King Herod had killed all the boy babies of Bethlehem, hoping to destroy Jesus, his spies still searched. They had heard stories of a family leaving at night on a donkey fleeing through the desert, and Herod sent them into Egypt too, to see if the rumors were true.

More than once the spies came uncomfortably close. They followed the holy family to the gilded city of Heliopolis, where stood tall pointed stone pillars called obelisks,

46

set there long before by the famous queen of Egypt, Cleopatra. (Someday those obelisks would be moved to Paris and London and Constantinople and New York and other great cities not even heard of then. Today in these cities you and I can look at the same stone monuments that Mary and Joseph and the Baby Jesus stared at with wide eyes so long ago!)

But Herod's spies lost track of the holy family. They did not find the Child in Heliopolis, and finally they went back across the desert to Jerusalem, to tell Herod they were sure the stories were not true, and that they believed the child King of Heaven was dead.

Mary and Joseph and Jesus found a tiny house near the obelisks, and took up their new life in Egypt. It was not easy for them. They did not speak the language of this place. And no one was very friendly to them because they were foreigners, and the Egyptians, like some people today, thought that anyone from another country could not be as nice or as wise as they.

The Egyptians believed in an army of hundreds of different gods; they did not know that there was only one true God. All around them the little family from Nazareth saw the tall stone statues of these false gods—of Ra, the god of the midday sun, and Isis the mother god, and Osiris the father god. They saw statues of horned bulls who were supposed to be gods, and of the sacred cat of Bubastes.

With the ugly statues towering over Him, Jesus learned to lisp His first prayer, a prayer to the Father in heaven. And in the loneliness of Egypt Mary leaned over the crib of the Baby who was the Son of God and chanted the ancient words of truth:

"Hear, O Israel! The Lord, our God, is one God!"

Nearly two years passed, and then once more an angel came to Joseph with great news:

"Arise," said the angel, "and take the Child and go

home to the land of Israel. For they are dead that tried to kill the Child."

At last, Herod was dead! Joseph began to pack at once. Taking the Child and mother on a donkey, he turned again to the gray and yellow desert that lay between them and home. They were going back to Nazareth, going home!

When Jesus learned to toddle, He followed His mother around the house and sang with her at her work. He played with chips of wood and little boats that Joseph carved for Him in the carpentry shop. And even as a little child He took time out to be alone, for His long, secret thoughts.

Time to stand, bread in hand by the open door and look knowingly into the sky and the soaring, creamy clouds. To lie in the field on a dewy morning, and press the moist grass against His cheek. To listen at the night window as if the wind spoke in whispers only He could understand. To smell Mother's hand, kneading the dough, and to taste, in long slow mouthfuls, the cool freshness of a cup of milk.

The child Jesus, because He was the Son of God, could hear and see and smell and taste and feel as no one else has ever been able to do—perfectly and beautifully and completely, the way we only wish we could. For Him colors were more brilliant, and the smell of new-mown grass was dizzyingly sweet, and birdsong so clear it brought tears to His eyes for the beauty of it.

"He sees more than we do, no matter what He looks at!" Joseph would say.

And Mary would smile as if to answer:

"And why not?"

Nor was Mary surprised at the way He made the birds and animals, and even the ugly little red worms, His friends. He loved all living things, for all things that live are made by God.

Nevertheless, Mary and Joseph saw to it that Jesus was

trained as all good children were, according to the laws God had given the Jews. Jesus was sent to school with all the other boys, just as if He were no different. Sitting on the floor of the synagogue, Jesus was taught the Scriptures and the prophets of His people—the same things we now read in what is called the Old Testament of the Bible. And at home, Jesus was taught His lessons, His manners, His skills.

"How do we dare to teach the Son of God anything?" asked Joseph once. "He knows everything, doesn't He?"

"God gave Him to us. God will show us how," said Mary. There were even then some boys and girls who thought they knew more than their parents, and who thought they did not need to obey the rules as ordinary people did. But Jesus, who truly knew more than anyone, obeyed His parents with a smile of love. He had come to earth to show us how to live, and part of living is knowing whom to obey.

The rules of family life which God had given to the Jews hundreds of years before were strict and hard, yet in the house of Mary and Joseph and Jesus every law was followed.

Like all their neighbors they ate only the food the Old Testament listed. They kept all the holy days and festivals. They recited prayers and sang psalms. And on the Sabbath day, they did no work, not even to light a fire, or peel a fruit, or tie a knot, or write a word, or wash a dog. All those laws and hundreds of others Jesus obeyed as a child.

Yet life for Jesus was not all rules and study. He was lean and strong of body, a swift runner, unafraid of climbing any height, or venturing into the darkest caves outside the town. He could shout as loud as the next boy and laugh as gleefully. No matter what happened, He was never known to snivel, to cry and have a runny nose or complain.

But Jesus was different in one way that even the dullest of His playmates could notice. He, who could always win at any test of strength, did not care about winning. He would wrestle or race with any boy, but He never lorded it over the one He defeated, and He never seemed to care about prizes or trophies. He played simply for the joy of playing, of using every muscle and fibre of His body.

That was true in His studies, too. His friends hated the whole idea of school, but boys in Nazareth had to go whether they liked it or not. Always Jesus read quickly and easily the scroll books with the writings of Moses and the prophets. It was as if He already knew the Scriptures, and only looked at them now to refresh His memory. In a short while He knew the writings by heart. After all, what could any teacher tell the Son of God that He did not already know? Yet Jesus never showed off His knowledge. He went through school quietly with all the others, doing the work expected of Him.

Sometimes Joseph would take Him on a picnic to the top of the highest hill above Nazareth and show the little Boy the land which was called Galilee. Galilee was a part of Palestine about fifty miles long and thirty-five miles wide, and now that King Herod was dead Galilee had its own special ruler, a son of the cruel Herod, whose name was Herod Antipas. From the hilltop Joseph and Jesus could see almost all of Galilee. Far away they could see the blue of the Mediterranean, and, nearer, the Valley of Jordan. Turning the other way they could spy the Sea of Galilee, and the mountains of Lebanon, and the snow like a chain of pearls around the high throat of Mount Hermon.

Then Joseph and Jesus would open Mary's picnic basket and munch awhile, and then lie on the grass on their backs, in silence.

And Jesus in His mind's eye would look far beyond Galilee, to lands and peoples of which Joseph did not even dream. The Boy on the warm grass of the hilltop saw in His heart the whole earth, and all the people one family, all children of God.

The Child Who Was Not Lost

WHEN Jesus was twelve years old, Mary and Joseph decided to take Him on a visit to Jerusalem to celebrate the wonderful holy springtime feast called the Passover. Every year the family made this journey so they could spend the holy time in the Temple, but this was the first time they would take Jesus with them. Jerusalem was a big city, and if a child should get lost how could anyone hope to find him? Still at twelve a boy is growing up, and can be trusted.

This time Anna and Joachim, His grandmother and grandfather, came with them, and as usual dozens of their friends and relatives from Nazareth with their older children too. The trip was long but gay, and the boys laughed and sang and ran back and forth from one family to another while the little brown donkeys plodded up and down the rocky hillsides. At night they camped by the wayside near a spring of water, and slept under the quivery spring stars.

Just to see the city was excitement enough for the boys. Their mouths gaped at the sight of so many people on the narrow cobbled streets—more people in one street than in all of Nazareth it seemed. Pilgrims came from all over to spend the holiday in Jerusalem, and they heard strange accents, and new languages everywhere they turned.

Jesus had not been to Jerusalem since He was an infant, the day Mary had carried Him into the Temple when He was less than six weeks old. That had been the day when the gnarled old Simeon had crept out of the shadows and called out for all to hear that this Baby was the Savior of the world. And after him had come the aged holy woman named Anna, declaring that Jesus was the Messiah. But Simeon and Anna had both passed away, and now no one in the Temple seemed to remember the words spoken twelve years before. Certainly no one noticed Jesus as He passed by.

With Mary and Joseph the tall young Lad walked into the Temple through the Gate that was called Beautiful. Knotted into the hem of His long white robe Jesus carried a few coins that Joseph had given Him. Mary had shown Him how to tie the copper coins into the cloth so that He would not lose them. With those pennies and mites He paid His own way into the Temple courts.

Joseph had explained to Jesus about money in the Temple. Because the Roman Empire had conquered this land only Roman coins, with a picture of Caesar, could be used for buying and selling. But the Temple was only for the Jews. The Roman Empire had no business there, and so inside the Temple only the old Jewish money could be used.

When people came into the Temple they had with them Roman money. Just inside the gate they changed their Roman silver into Jewish money.

"And," added Joseph sadly, "we always lose money when we do. The money-changers keep some of the money for themselves when they change it. That is how they get rich!"

"Why do people need money in the Temple of God?"

"To buy sacrifices! One must pay for doves and pigeons and lambs to offer them up to God. And you have to pay five times what they are worth," said Joseph.

Jesus listened and said nothing, but He grew very thoughtful.

Jesus and Joseph walked together into the inner parts of the Temple. Mary and Anna went into another part, for the women were not allowed to sit with the men. Jesus looked at the shining altar. There, thirteen years before, Zachary, now dead, had seen an angel and had lost his voice. The boy Jesus counted the twelve steps before the altar, and admired the gilded doorway, and hanging from its gilt rod, the veil of the Temple, a many-colored curtain. Gold spikes on the flat roof glittered in the sunset, and just over the doorway was a gleaming bunch of golden grapes.

Wherever Jesus looked there were priests. The place swarmed with men in ceremonial costume—Levites with pointed caps and large pockets in which they carried the books of the law; Pharisees with deep white fringes on their purple gowns; and with them from Galilee and Judea and the land beyond Jordan crowds of good believers who came to buy lambs or pigeons to offer at the altar. The air was full of the smell of burning offerings, and the smoke of incense.

Jesus heard the voice of the Temple choir and the sounding trumpets. The music of harps softened His dark eyes. He watched the people kneel and pray, and heard the psalms they sang, and they made Him glad.

But why did the people burn the doves and the lambs on the altars? Why did they imagine God would be pleased? Why did the poor have to spend their money to buy animals? Did not such ideas really insult the goodness of the Idea of God?

One of the prophets, Amos, had told the people that God did not want burnt offerings or feasts—that all He wanted was to see His people just and righteous and good. Yet everyone in the Temple seemed to have forgotten that. It was time they remembered!

Suddenly Jesus stood up, while Joseph still prayed with closed eyes. The Boy strode eagerly into another part of the Temple, and no one saw Him go.

In another part of the Temple sat all the most learned men, who were called Doctors because they were so wise.

They knew every word of the Scriptures, and could tell every law that God had made, and they loved God sincerely. But though they knew everything about the laws they did not know much about love, for God or for others. They did not like to talk about how people should live with each other, about honesty and fair play and kindness. They sat in a circle and read the prophets and argued about what they meant, and their minds were far away from the little problems of everyday life.

Around them sat more men, listening in silence while the Doctors spoke. Not one of them would have dared to interrupt.

Suddenly, without a word of introduction, the twelve-year-old Boy from Nazareth walked into the center of this circle of whitebeards, and slowly began asking questions.

No one knew who He was. They did not even know His name, but something about Him made them listen. At first they were ready to laugh at the idea of a young boy's

challenging them. Then, as they listened they grew amazed at all He knew about the Scriptures, and the law, and the prophets. And the questions He asked! They sounded simple, childlike even, and yet they were the wisest and deepest questions ever heard.

Jesus had come to ask them only one thing:

You who are teachers, who are so wise in Scriptures, what do you know of God?

And they did not know that the Boy who asked was Himself the Son of God! They knew only that His tongue seemed on fire with truth, and they found themselves listening to the unknown Child as if they were children, and He the teacher.

They spoke in long, complicated words, and said things they themselves scarcely understood. And Jesus spoke in simple words so that all could understand, as He explained to them that they had forgotten a very important truth. They had forgotten that though God has laws which we must obey,

He cares more about what is in our hearts. One kind, good thing we do means more to God than a hundred lambs burnt on an altar, or seventy-seven rules obeyed with no loving smile behind them.

A night passed, and a new day turned into night, and the fifteen men were still trying to answer the Boy no one knew. When the older men grew tired and hungry new Doctors took their places, but Jesus never seemed to need sleep. As another day dawned they still talked, fifteen wise men, and one wiser Boy.

And all the time Jesus kept saying one thing, over and over in different words. Sometimes He would use the words of one of the old prophets, whose name was Micah:

"What does God ask of you, except that you live justly and well, and love kindness, and walk humbly with your God?"

No one noticed how time had sped until Jesus, looking over the heads of the men, saw the pale face of Mary, His mother. Tears were in her eyes. Quietly she spoke to Him:

"Son, why have You done so to us? Your father and I have been looking for You—sorrowing because You were lost."

At once Jesus made His farewell to the Doctors. He wrapped Mary's blue cloak around her shoulders, and took her hand, and led her toward the gate.

As they walked she told Him what had happened.

"When Joseph finished praying and saw You were gone, he thought You were with Your grandfather, or Your friends, and so he did not worry. And so did I. When we started back to Nazareth we were sure You were with us— maybe with the other boys. But last night we could not find You anywhere."

Mary shook her head sadly at her Son. "You don't know how we wept. How could You run away without a word? How could You treat us like that?"

Jesus looked into His mother's eyes and said with a tender smile:

"Why did you look for Me? Did you not know that I must be about My Father's business?"

And neither Joseph nor Mary could really understand what He said to them. Joseph understood in part. He knew that he was only the foster father of Jesus, and that God was His real Father. So Jesus had been about God's business.

But why had He not told them He must talk with those learned men, instead of letting them think He was lost?

"Perhaps," Mary thought, "it is because even now when He tells us, we do not understand. We never understand all that God does. And remember—this Child is God."

For a moment Mary and Joseph stared at Him, puzzled and worried—but only for that moment, and then suddenly He was their boy again. He hugged His mother, and kissed the gray and golden beard of Joseph.

They need not worry. All the rest of His youth Jesus obeyed them. He went home with them to Nazareth, and Mary watched Him grow into strong manhood as the years passed.

But she never forgot that day in the Temple, nor the words He had spoken to her. She was learning that even those very close to God do not understand the reason for all He does.

The Voice in the Wilderness

FOR eighteen years, until Jesus was thirty, He and Mary lived in Nazareth. Changes came while Jesus was growing to manhood. Joseph, the strong patient carpenter who had been as a father to Him, died, and so did Jesus' grandparents Joachim and Anna. For His mother and Himself Mary's Son earned a living carrying on the work in the carpenter shop. Many a neighbor in Nazareth ate off a table built by Jesus, or slept in a bed He had made. Under His hands and loving eye the plainest wood shone as He fashioned a cradle for a new baby, or a doll or a boat for the dark-eyed boys and girls who played near the town well.

The men and women of Nazareth liked Jesus well enough—who could help but smile when He smiled?—but they did not see much of Him. He kept to Himself a great deal, and when He was not at work among the sawdust and shavings, no one was sure where He went, or what He did while other men sat talking around the caravan fires, or drinking in the taverns.

"He is not much like other carpenters," they said. "He seems always to be waiting for something—or getting ready for something."

Indeed, that was just what Jesus was doing. He was preparing for the day when He would no longer be a small-town carpenter. The time was coming, He knew, when He must put away hammer and saw, leave His mother and His home, and go about the real work He had to do. He knew that He had been born for only one reason—to bring people nearer to God, and to offer them new life of hope and happiness in this world and in heaven.

When He was through in the carpenter shop He would go alone to the hillside outside town to think, to dream and to pray, to be ready for the years when He would go out into the world to teach man how to live. He had grown to manhood Himself, now, this Son of God. Sturdy and tall, He stood on the hill looking down in Nazareth. His hair was soft and golden-brown and hung around His shoulders in the way that all men wore their hair then. He had His mother's glorious dark eyes. His muscles were strong from hard work. He was God, it was true, but He was also a real man, the most perfect man that ever lived.

That was the amazing secret of Jesus, that He was both God and man. No one could ever say to Him:

"All very easy for You to tell us what to do and what not to do. But You don't know how hard it is to be good all the time!"

Jesus knew. He had been a boy, a child like everyone else. He had been a teen-ager. And He had been a workingman. He knew what life was like in the poorest home, in the schools and the streets and in the shops. He was almost ready to start to teach. But there was one more thing He must do . . . .

Suddenly a strange piece of news came to Nazareth, news of a strong man from the wilderness of Judea, who was preaching in the towns of the South and blessing people by dipping them in the water of the River Jordan. The man's name, they said, was John.

"That John is Your cousin," said Mary to Jesus. "He is the son of Cousin Zachary and Cousin Elizabeth."

And what was John saying in the towns of the South? He was telling great crowds that He was sent by God to announce the Savior of the world!

Jesus listened as the bearded travelers and bright-robed merchants from the South told more about this John.

"He is a giant, almost—so strong, so powerful he is. They say when his folks died—they were very, very old, you remember—he went to live in a cave in the desert by himself."

"He lived in the rocks in that terrible bleak valley below Jerusalem, near the Dead Sea. And he ate only locusts and wild honey!" said a camel driver.

"You should see him! He wears the skins of wild beasts, and a cloak made of camel hair. His hair and beard are long and tangled, and the desert sun has made his skin the color of bronze."

"He stands outside the towns and shouts at the people, telling them to stop living such bad lives, and do good. And he says some strange things."

"What does he say?"

"He says: 'The kingdom of heaven is at hand.' No one is sure what that means, exactly. But they know what he means about leading bad lives," said the camel driver.

"And then he asks those who are sorry that they have broken God's laws to wade into the Jordan River and let him splash them with water. He baptizes them, as a sign that they want to wash away all the evil things they have done."

Jesus listened to these tales in silence, but the other men of Nazareth wanted to know more. They had read the prophecies of a Savior who would come. And they asked:

"Who is John? Could he be the Savior, the Christ?"

The camel driver shook his head. "No. We have asked him, and he says: 'I, indeed, baptize you with water. But there shall come One mightier than I, whose sandal I am not even worthy to untie. He shall baptize you with the Holy Ghost—and with fire.' "

When Jesus had heard all they said about John, He sighed and laid down His carpenter tools. He said a tender goodbye to Mary and started off alone, on foot. He was going from Galilee to the wilderness, to see for Himself.

After days of walking He came to a desolate land, where the mountainsides were bare and nothing grew, and only pebbles and broken stones met the eye. Out of the wilderness He hurried, down to the green willows and reeds beside the Jordan River. Near the bank of the narrow, muddy river a crowd of people stood silent to hear John speak.

Jesus made His way to the front. Calmly He stood before John, the cousin He had not seen since they were both little boys. For a long moment neither one spoke. The crowd watched them, wondering what this meeting meant.

In a voice so low only John could hear, Jesus said that He wanted His cousin to baptize Him.

John was shocked. "But it is I who should be baptized by You," he objected. "And You come to me?"

Jesus lifted His head and said with a disarming smile: "Let it be so now."

The two cousins walked together into the tumbling river, and Jesus let John baptize Him with the water of the Jordan.

When it was over, Jesus looking up through dripping eyes, saw a white dove flying over His head, hovering, pausing in the air with fluttering wings. The bird lighted on His shoulder, and in it He knew that the Spirit of God had appeared to Him. And many in the watching crowd heard a voice from heaven say:

"This is My beloved Son, in Whom I am well pleased."

Jesus pressed John's hand in farewell. Then telling no one what He meant to do, He made His way quickly through the crowd, back to the wilderness alone.

He was going into the desert to face a great and lonely test. Into the place where no water ran and no leaves grew, where only the red-tailed buzzards wheeled overhead, Jesus went to learn how it feels to suffer as men suffer.

He knew that sometimes the devil comes to all of us, to the young and the old, to tempt us to do evil things—to lie, or to cheat, or to disobey, or even to turn our backs on God, and laugh at all who are good. He knew too that evil thoughts often come when we are tired, or hungry, or lonely and weak, and then they are very hard to fight. And because Jesus was a man as well as God, He knew He must show us all that He knew how hard it could be to do battle against temptation.

He went to a cave in a hillside in that bleak desert. He went alone, with no food. He stayed there for forty days, not eating anything, not even a crust of bread. And during those days, the little home at Nazareth and the blessed face of Mary His mother seemed very far away.

After these forty days Jesus was exhausted, and ready to faint with hunger. Never was any man weaker, or more lonely, or more friendless, than He. And that was the time that Satan came to Him, to tempt Him to do wrong.

Jesus was God. He could have sent the devil away. But we, who are not God, have to face the devil. Every day we have to choose whether to do good, or to listen to the voice of evil, and do what we know is wrong. And so Jesus who came to earth as a man to teach us how to live, let the devil tempt Him, as he tempts us.

Jesus was hungry, more hungry than any man or child has ever been. So the devil came to Him and said:

"If You are really the Son of God, why not turn those stones into bread?"

Jesus could have done that. But He said: "Man does not live by bread alone, but by every word that comes from the mouth of God."

Then the devil took Him to the edge of a steep cliff and said: "If You are the Son of God, throw Yourself down, and let the angels save You with their hands." And the devil meant, You live like any ordinary man and yet You are God. Why not show the world what tremendous miracles You can do?

But Jesus knew that we would love and understand Him better if He lived as a perfect Man, without miracles to save Himself from unhappiness, and He refused to do what the devil asked.

Then the devil took Him up onto another high mountain, and showed Him all the kingdoms of the world and all the glory of them, and said to Jesus:

"I will give You all this, if You will do all the evil things I say, and adore me."

And Jesus said to him: "The Lord your God shall you adore and you shall serve only Him. Satan—be gone!"

And the devil left. The test was over.

Now Jesus knew what it was like to be tempted. Now when He told men not to listen to the devil, but to serve only God, men would remember that He knew how hard that was to do.

Jesus was thin, and pale and haggard when those torturing forty days were over, but God had sent His angels down to care for His Son after the devil had left. Then slowly He walked back toward the Jordan River. The hot desert lay behind Him, and the cool wind felt good on His perspiring face. In His sunburned hands He held wild dates, eating at last after nearly six weeks with no food.

The time had nearly come for Jesus to start His work.

The First Disciples

THE morning after He returned from His forty days in the desert, Jesus took a walk by the River Jordan. On a low grassy hill He came face to face with that giant John, called the Baptist. At the sight of his Cousin the Baptist threw out his arms in greeting, and murmured:

"Behold! Here is He who takes away the sins of the world! This is the Son of God!"

That day and others Jesus lingered, watching John, and listening to his speeches, and talking with him in lonely walks at night. Men and women from all over the country were coming to hear John the Baptist, and the crowds by the river were very great.

On one bright morning there stood in the crowd two fishermen from the North. One was Andrew, a sturdy man with a good head for business. His friend was named John, a good-looking, stormy young man. The two earned their living fishing in the Sea of Galilee, and they had come together to hear John the Baptist. For some days they stayed and listened to all the Baptist had to say, and finally this sunny morning they spoke to him.

"You are fishermen from Galilee?" the Baptist asked in surprise. "Why did you travel this long way—just to listen to me?"

Andrew answered. "We earn very little money, and most of that we must pay in taxes. We cannot even afford to eat the fish we catch. A dog's life is better than ours. Then someone told us that you were telling men the secret of a happy life. So we tried you."

The Baptist, tall and brown in his ragged clothes, said: "And have I helped you?"

Then the Baptist pointed over their shoulders to where Jesus walked alone, coming toward them. He whispered to the two fishermen:

"Look! There is the real Lamb of God!"

The two fishermen gasped. They had heard those words before, in the Scriptures. "The Lamb of God" meant the Savior!

"I saw the Spirit of God come down to Him like a dove when I baptized Him with water," said John the Baptist. "This is the Son of God!"

And John the Baptist smiled at the young fishermen.

"If you hope to find the true meaning of life, and the secret of happiness—follow Him!"

Quickly Andrew and John hurried after the tall, lithe figure of Jesus, who was already walking down the sunlit street. At the sound of their footsteps Jesus slowed down and looked over His shoulder, then turned and faced them. He laid a hand on Andrew's shoulder, and smiled at John.

"Looking for someone?" He asked. And the way He smiled at them showed that He understood all that was in their hearts.

Jesus explained to them that He was planning to travel all over Palestine talking to all the people who had problems and unhappiness, just like Andrew and John. He would need helpers. But He wanted only men who would stay with Him, who understood Him, and believed what He said. Andrew and John could help Him if they wished—but first they must spend hours and days studying and listening while He taught them His message. He was not merely asking them to give Him a part of their time. He needed their lives! Their souls! So they must make sure. If, in the end, they did believe, they could join Him.

Andrew and John looked into His eyes:

"Master," they said. "Show us where You live and we will go there with You right now!"

"Come and see!"

Jesus led the way to His lodgings in a hut outside the town. From twilight till dawn the three sat together, while Jesus taught them. Day and night passed as they listened, and asked questions, and listened again, and finally they were sure. More than anything in the world they wanted to follow Him. They not only believed Him, they loved Him heart and soul.

Andrew asked one last question:

"Master, all that You speak about—a life of love and sacrifice, and closeness with the Father in heaven—sounds wonderful to us. But we have the old law of Israel, given to us by God. Have You come to change the law?"

Jesus shook His head slowly.

"No, Andrew, I come not to change the law—but to fulfill it!"

The two fishermen turned to each other, wondering. What did those words mean? That He was the Messiah, the Savior? He had not said so. They did not ask. They would wait and see.

"Master," said John, "we shall go with You. You have warned us that Your ideas are dangerous. Let them be so! They are worth dying for!"

Then Andrew told Jesus that he had a brother that he would like the Master to meet, and ran off to find him.

Andrew found his older brother, whose name was Simon, washing his feet at the town fountain. Simon was a tall, broad, bulging man with huge shoulders and a rugged

beard. His eyes were bright and fierce, and his face was cross and tired.

"Simon!"

"Hey? Oh, so it's you. Where have you been, and why are you panting and grunting so, Andrew?"

"I'm out of breath, that's all Simon. We have found Him! And I ran all the way to tell you about Him!"

"Who has found what?"

"John and I."

"John and you have found what?"

"The most wonderful new Teacher in the world. He knows the answer to every question you can think of."

"What on earth are you talking about, Andrew? And who wants a teacher? We're grown men!"

"Simon, we have found a Messenger of God. I am sure of it."

Simon pulled his beard and shook his head and wrinkled his freckled nose.

"Don't believe a word of it," he growled. "You two are getting sillier all the time. First you run after John the Baptist. You think *he's* the one. Then he tells you in plain words he is not. Now you think it's someone else!"

"Come and see for yourself," said Andrew.

Simon finished drying his enormous toes.

"All right. I will go with you, and see."

It was twilight when the two brothers came to the hut where John still sat listening to Jesus. As the great hulk of Simon filled the entrance and his shadow fell at the feet of the Master, Jesus' face seemed to light up in welcome for the bearded fisherman.

Jesus stood and embraced him.

"You are Simon, son of Jona! But you shall be called Peter."

And the way He spoke the others felt that He meant much more than He was saying.

The first three were there, the first of twelve men who would be the Lord's disciples. All these, and Jesus too, were from Galilee, and they started now to walk with Him back to the land they had come from. But they had hardly begun the long journey north over the stony road when their number began to grow.

The first to join them was a young man named Philip whom they happened to find walking the same highway. Philip was a friend of Andrew, and he too was a fisherman. Jesus welcomed him instantly, and when Philip heard what the Master had to say, he wanted at once to join the new disciples.

"Not only that, Master. I have a friend whom I should like to bring to You. May I get him?"

Just then a line of camels passed down the highway, brass bells jingling from their harnesses. Philip begged the driver for a ride on one, and hurried ahead. A few miles down the highway he found his friend, whose name was Nathanael Bartholomew, lying under a fig tree staring at the sky.

"Nathanael!" called Philip, as the camel kneeled to let him off. "We have found a most wonderful Teacher. He might even be the Man the Scriptures promised. The Messiah, perhaps!"

"Really, now," laughed Nathanael. "Wonderful, wonderful. What makes you think you'd find the Messiah on a rocky road like this? Who is he?"

"His name is Jesus."

"Yes—and where is he from?"

"From Nazareth."

Nathanael laughed lazily. "Come now—would a great and wonderful teacher come from such a small town as Nazareth? Can anything good come from Nazareth?"

"You'd better come and see!" ordered Philip, yanking Nathanael to his feet. He grabbed Nathanael's arm and pulled him down the road like a prisoner, until they saw Jesus and His other friends coming.

Jesus waved to Nathanael from a distance. "Nathanael! Before Philip called you, when you were under the fig tree, I saw you."

Nathanael blinked. He *had* been under the fig tree. But that was miles beyond, where Jesus could not possibly have seen him. He stammered:

"Master . . ."

But Jesus put a friendly arm about him. "Because I said to you that I saw you under the fig tree, you believe!"

Jesus lifted His bearded chin toward the sky, and calmly He promised: "Greater things than these you shall see."

But on that day on the highway, Nathanael Bartholomew saw only the face of Jesus, and knew he would follow this Master till he died.

And with His five new disciples, Jesus walked the highway to Galilee, the first part of the long road they would all travel together.

What Happened at the Wedding

JESUS led His five new followers back to His home in Nazareth. He found His household in a state of excitement and happy confusion. The daughter of one of Mary's friends was getting married that very day, and Mary was planning to go over and help serve the wedding feast.

She was scurrying around the house getting ready when Jesus and His friends came to the door, without so much as a word to warn her. Eyes shining, Mary made them all welcome—Peter, Andrew, John, Philip, and Nathanael too. Five extra men would be a handful in the little home, but whatever Jesus did was right in Mary's eyes. His friends were her friends, and she made room for them.

"Will you all come to the wedding with me?" she asked. "The family lives in the village of Cana."

"I come from Cana!" said Nathanael happily.

"Good. Perhaps you will know them. I have promised to go and help them celebrate," said Mary.

Jesus and His friends were a little tired after walking all the way from the Jordan to Nazareth, but after they washed and rested they turned and walked with Mary five miles more down the road. Near sunset they came into the town of Cana.

Cana was not the most beautiful of towns. It was a jigsaw jumble of stone houses and huts made out of dried mud. Only the few well-to-do families had gardens, with cypress trees and olive groves. The narrow streets were crowded with men wearing the desert cloak with a hood, the robe we call a

70

burnoose. Camels lumbered over the dust and cobblestones. Women with veiled faces wobbled along perched sideways on little gray donkeys. Here and there they saw little children carrying lambs, or playing hide-and-seek among the tents in the bazaar.

This evening nearly the whole town seemed to be going to the wedding feast, and the evening air shook with excitement and music and song. Jesus did not often go to parties of this kind. He had always been too thoughtful, too studious, to have time for parties. But tonight He had a happy time. He and the five disciples put away all thoughts of their serious talks about God and heaven and how to live, and enjoyed themselves like everyone else at the feast.

The sound of harps and flutes filled the night, and the young people danced in their finest clothes. The tables were covered with the best of meats and fruits, and wine to drink, and laughter and happiness seemed to bubble around the beautiful dark-eyed young bride and her tall, black-haired groom. The family had spared no expense. They had even hired a caterer, a man whose job it was to provide wine and food and waiters and dishes and chairs for all the guests, since no family would ever own enough to take care of such a crowd. The caterer bustled around busily, and none of the gay guests noticed that he wore a worried frown.

The fun was at its height when suddenly Mary came to Jesus, and led Him aside to a corner where no one could overhear them. Her eyes were troubled.

"They have no more wine," she whispered. "So many people came, more than they expected—You and Your five friends and many others—and now the wine is about gone, and the party is only just starting. The caterer does not know what to do. There just is no more wine."

Mary smiled. "They are such a nice young couple, and they would be so embarrassed to have to tell their guests they had no more to give them."

Jesus took His mother's hand, and looked into her eyes.

"What is that to Me? And to you? My hour is not yet come," He said.

They were strange words, but Mary knew what He meant. She was asking Him to help this family. Only by a miracle could He help them. There was nowhere to buy wine, now. And Jesus was reminding her that the moment He performed a miracle, the story of it would fly over the land, and everyone would be coming to Him. His time of quiet, and of getting ready would be over. And that would mean taking the first step toward the cross.

Did she really want a miracle now—just so that wedding guests might have more to drink?

Mary knew His thoughts. She knew what a miracle that evening would mean. But she felt so sorry for the young bride and groom, and their family and their guests. She had asked, for their sake. The answer was up to her Son, and she knew He would listen to her plea. Never would He refuse her.

She turned away, and went to the waiters, and told them simply, "Whatever He tells you to do—do it!"

Jesus walked to the back of the room. There He found the six stone water pots which were part of the furnishings of all homes in Palestine, kept there to be used in special religious purifying ceremonies. With His hand He called the waiters.

"Fill the water pots with water," He said.

They were too polite to let Him see how ridiculous they thought that idea was. Why bother filling pots with water, when what they needed was wine, they wondered. Still, they did as He asked, filling the pots to the brim with clear, fresh water.

"Now take some out of the pots," said Jesus, "and bring it to the caterer."

The waiters dipped a ladle into one pot, and brought it out full. They looked at it and gasped.

"The color has changed!" they shouted. "Look! The water is red!"

"It looks like wine. But it *was* water!"

The caterer heard them shouting and rushed over to see what all the fuss was about. He had been so busy worrying that he had not noticed what went on in the corner. The waiters held the ladle for him to see and taste. With raised eyebrows and a wrinkled nose he sipped it. Then his eyes popped wide open.

"It is fine wine. The finest!"

And the caterer did not know what Jesus had done. The waiters tried to tell him, but he was too busy to listen. He thought the bride's father had been hiding the wine in the water pots, and he hurried over to him at once, a little cross because he had not been told that there was plenty of wine.

"What is happening here?" he asked. "Every man serves the best wine first, at the beginning of the party, and then later when everybody has had some to drink he brings out the wine that is not so good. But you have kept the good wine until now. It is the best I have ever tasted in all my forty years as a caterer in Galilee!"

Soon everybody in the room was talking about the wonderful wine, and finally the waiters made themselves heard, and told how Jesus had changed the water into wine right before their eyes. But when the bride's father and the bride and groom and the guests went to thank Him, Jesus was gone.

He and His disciples were walking back to Nazareth. Because Jesus was silent, His friends did not speak. But in their hearts they marveled at their Master, and because they had seen His first miracle they believed.

The Woman at the Well

THE five men who had become disciples of Jesus sat one night talking alone among themselves. Ever since they had met Him they had followed Him, listening as He taught them on long walks through the countryside. They loved Him, and they loved the things He taught them of the goodness and mercy of God. But they had much more to learn, more than they dreamed.

"What do you think of Him, really?" asked Philip. "Do you think Jesus is the Messiah, the Savior? We have never dared to ask Him. And He has never said."

"Perhaps. All I know is that He is a great teacher, and a good man. I feel He is my best friend," said Nathanael.

"Maybe He is the Messiah. Or maybe God sent Him as a messenger, a teacher," said Andrew.

"He understands so much. He knows everything," said John.

"I do not know what or who He is. But I know He is the dearest friend I could have. Like—a brother," said Peter.

None of these five men knew that Jesus was the Son of God, part of God. Jesus had not yet told them that secret, because He knew it was too soon for them to believe such a wonderful, mysterious thing. First He must teach them the

ideas which God wanted them to learn, and then when they
understood, He could tell them who He was. And from the
beginning Jesus found that the best way to teach a lesson
was not to tell people what to do, but to show them.

The first lesson He taught them was one of the hardest for men to learn. It was the lesson of love.

One day with His five disciples Jesus was coming from
a visit to a town called Jericho, on his way back to Galilee.
And this time, He told them, they would go home by a different road. They would go through Samaria.

The five men stared at each other in amazement, and
when they were alone they whispered to each other:

"Why does He want to go through Samaria? No one
goes there. For hundreds and hundreds of years the Jews
and the Samaritans have hated each other."

"Samaritans are terrible people! No decent person
should have anything to do with them!"

And the five shook their heads, wondering why the
Master wanted to go near the land of the people they hated.
But they said nothing to Him, and when He was ready they
followed Him, grumbling, into Samaria.

Jesus led them straight into Samaria. Once inside the
forbidden land He did not rest till He reached its most famous spot, the well of Jacob, said by many to be the oldest
well in the world.

By now the five disciples could tell when Jesus wanted
to be alone, and since it was late afternoon they went on by
themselves to buy food for the evening meal. And as they
went they wondered whether the Samaritans would even sell
it to them, or whether a fight might break out when they
came into the village.

Meanwhile Jesus sat alone on the stone rim around the
old well. Presently a woman came toward Him with a jug
slung over her shoulder, a green hood thrown back from
her head. She pretended not to see Him at all, and busied

herself tying a rope to the jug and letting it down into the well to fill it with water.

Suddenly Jesus spoke to her. "Give Me a drink," He said.

The woman pulled up her dripping jug and set it on the stone. She looked at Jesus in silence. She could see He was not a Samaritan, but a Jew. And she knew that no Jew would ever ask a Samaritan like herself for any kind of help, let alone for a drink of water. And so she asked:

"Why do You, a Jew, ask me for a drink—me, a Samaritan?"

Jesus smiled gently. "If you knew who I am perhaps *you* would have asked *Me* for a drink, and I would have given you living water."

The woman was truly puzzled, and she put the back of her hand to her head as she said, "Sir, You have no jug or pail, and the well is deep. Where would You get this living water?"

Leaning forward, Jesus said: "Whoever drinks this water will thirst again. But anyone who drinks the water I will give him shall not ever thirst again."

The woman smiled unbelievingly. Then Jesus leaned further forward and whispered in her ear, telling her a secret about herself, a secret of some wrong-doing in her past, which she had thought no one else in the whole world knew. Her face grew pale and she backed away from Him.

"Sir," she gasped. "I see that You are a prophet. I know that the Messiah is coming who is called Christ. When He comes He will tell us all things."

Jesus stood up and looked at her and said:

"I am He."

The woman looked at Him—and turned and ran, leaving her water jug behind her, and ran off to the city where she told everyone she met that the Christ, the Messiah, was out at Jacob's well. Jesus had not even told His disciples

Who He really was. The first person in the world whom He told was this woman, a Samaritan.

Just then Peter and John, Nathanael, Andrew and Philip all came back, their arms filled with bundles of food.

Jesus looked at the packages and said:

"I have meat to eat which you do not know."

"Has someone else brought You something to eat?"

Jesus threw an arm over the shoulder of Peter, who looked most puzzled of them all:

"My meat is doing the will of God who sent Me—that I may perfect His work."

Suddenly they heard a great noise, and crowds of Samaritans surrounded them, loudly demanding to see the stranger Jew who had talked with their townswoman. She had told them everything, and they were trooping out to see the Man she said was the Messiah. At first the disciples were alarmed, fearing a fight, but then they saw smiles on the approaching faces.

When the Samaritans saw Jesus, and spoke with Him, they pleaded with Him not to leave them. They made Him their guest, serving Him their favorite bread, little oval cakes of wheat, and bowls of meat stew with a most savory smell, and milk and wine. And, as was the custom in those days, they washed His feet to show Him He was welcome to their homes.

And Jesus taught them, and with them, His five disciples. He taught them about the Kingdom of Heaven. And He taught them that the finest things a man can do are to love God and to love all the other people God has made. He told them that all the men and women and children in the world are children of God, the Father—and for that reason they should all love each other like brothers. And nowhere on earth should men hate other men.

For years the Jews and Samaritans had hated each other, but Jesus, a Jew, had come to the Samaritans first, be-

fore all others, to tell them His message. And He stayed with
them for two days. It was a visit, and a lesson, they would
never forget.

And never again did Peter or John, or Philip or Andrew or Nathanael speak badly of the Samaritans.

The Rich Man's Son

IN one bedroom of the blue and gold mansion in the seaside town of Capernaum the shutters were closed. Inside on a bed of softest down lay a boy of twelve years, his freckled face crimson with fever. He twisted and tossed on his bed, so sick he seemed not even to know his mother's voice when she spoke to him.

The table by his bed was crowded with medicines, shining bottles of red liquids and jars of black ointment and of gray and green and yellow powders. Four doctors in embroidered robes stood beside him, pulling gravely at their beards.

"Five days and six nights we have watched your son in this illness. We have tried everything," they said. "But we cannot make your son well."

The boy's father, the richest and most powerful man in Capernaum, rose from his seat by the door.

"You *must* make him well. He is my son—and I love him," he said.

"We can do nothing more for him," said the doctors sadly.

The father paced up and down the room, his eyes filling with tears.

"I would spend a fortune to help my boy," he said.

"Isn't there any new medicine, or a new doctor you could call?"

"None," said the physicians.

"Somewhere there must be someone who could help!" said the father.

The boy's mother, sitting on the edge of the bed, looked up.

"I have heard of a person named Jesus of Nazareth," she said. "And what I have heard has been strange and wonderful. They say He was just a carpenter but that He has become a great teacher who speaks of God as if He knows Him. Only God can save our child. Could you find this Man called Jesus?"

The father stopped still. "I will find Him," he said.

And so it was that the richest man in Capernaum went alone onto the highways, asking the poorest men he met where he could find the One called Jesus.

Meanwhile, Jesus and His band of five men had left Samaria and started back to Galilee through the sweetness of a May morning. Flocks of storks flew squonking overhead, and land tortoises crept slowly across the road, sure signs that spring had come to Palestine.

Everywhere He went crowds gathered around Jesus to hear Him speak, sometimes on street corners, sometimes in synagogues, or on a farm by the wayside.

"Repent!" He would say, looking into their eyes as if He could see every wrong thing that they had ever done— the lie that man had told, the angry tongue of that woman in green, the penny the little blue-eyed boy had stolen. Tell God you are sorry, He was saying, and ask Him to help you to be good. Love goodness, and turn your back on what you know is wrong.

"Repent and believe," He said. Believe that God is good, and that He loves you, and that you must love Him.

Believe that God will watch over you, and guard you, and that if you do His will, and live a good life, no evil can hurt you. Believe that though it may be hard to do what God wants, the reward is great, and His help is greater.

Wherever He went Jesus brought three gifts that could not be seen—the gifts of love, and of hope, and of courage. And the people who heard Him could hardly talk of anything but Jesus. Women, picking beans in the garden, talked of how kind He was to all who came to tell Him their troubles. Farmers in their fields, doing battle against the grasshoppers and locusts who threatened their crops, and hunters in the hills trapping deer and partridge, and the miller, and the hired men, and the traders in the market place all talked about Jesus.

On that gentle May day Jesus and His five disciples stopped to rest by the road not far from Nazareth. Immediately a crowd surrounded them—some to listen, some to stare, and others hoping to tell Jesus their problems, and ask Him what to do. The sun was hot, for it was a little after noon, and there was little shade under the fig trees. And as always in a crowd, the gabble of their voices was enough to make you wish you had no ears.

Then suddenly they fell silent. Down the road and straight through the crowd came a stranger.

The crowd stared at him. They saw his necklace of

watery-blue aquamarines, black opals, and grass-green emeralds. They smelled the perfumed oil on his curly hair. Obviously he was a rich man, a nobleman high in the court of King Herod. But why was he on foot, and alone? There was dust speckled over his fine clothes, and his face was pale, and perspiring.

He walked directly up to Jesus. "I have heard strange stories about You," he said. "I have heard that You make miracles, that You made a fountain of wine at Cana. And

that at Jacob's well in Samaria You read the secrets of a woman's mind."

He stopped to catch his breath, then went on, "I need help. I come from Capernaum. My son is there—very ill. The doctors say he will die. Please—will You come down and heal my son?"

"Unless you *see* miracles and wonders, you will not believe," replied Jesus, watching the man's face closely.

"Lord—come down before my son dies!" pleaded the father, and he broke into sobs.

Jesus closed His eyes. Softly He spoke:

"Go your way! Your son lives."

The rich man looked up into Jesus' face, and believed what He said. His eyes spoke his thanks, and without another word he turned and ran through the crowd, and raced down the open road toward Capernaum. And when he left Jesus and started home it was what was then called the seventh hour of the day, or what we would call one o'clock in the afternoon.

The road from Nazareth to Capernaum is long. The rich man ran as far as he could, and then panting for breath he slowed down to a walk. But he did not stop, not even for a drink of water. Hour after hour he trudged on through the dust, hurrying home to his son.

Night came, and he stopped on a stretch of grass for a few hours' rest.

I believe what Jesus said, he thought to himself as he watched the moon rise over the hills. Perhaps my friends would call me a fool to believe the words of an ex-carpenter from Nazareth—but though He did not say so, I know He is more than that. It is hard to believe, that just by asking Him my son could get well—but I know it is true. Without even seeing the boy, I know it. And he laughed for pure happiness, and scrambled to his feet, and hurried on homeward through the night.

At last by morning light he saw the walls of his home, and outside, waiting for him, were his servants. They ran to greet him.

"Your son is well! The doctors say he will live!"

"Praise God!" said the rich man. "At what hour did he get better?"

"Yesterday, at the seventh hour, the fever left him."

At the seventh hour—one o'clock in the afternoon! The exact moment the father remembered when Jesus had said to him: "Your son lives!"

The father climbed the stairs three at a time, and dashed into his son's room. The bed was empty. The boy, standing by the window, was busy fixing a kite. He looked up and grinned.

"I'm well, father. All well."

"I know. And I must tell you why you are well," said the father.

And so that twelve-year-old boy became the first person in history to hear the amazing truth that if you ask Jesus to help you, and believe that He will, your prayer will be answered. The answer may not come when you expect it, or in the way you expect, but if you believe in Him, He will help you without fail.

"But you must *believe,* heart and soul, and trust Him, without waiting to see His answer first," said the father.

The boy stood straight and tall. "I believe in Jesus— though I have never seen Him. And perhaps somehow I can help others to believe, other children who must learn to love and trust Him without ever seeing Him for themselves."

The Fishermen

JESUS and His five friends—Peter and Andrew, John, Philip and Nathanael—were walking to Capernaum. That famous city glittering over the Sea of Galilee was the home of the rich man's son Jesus had cured, but it was also the hometown of four of the new disciples. Peter and Andrew lived there, and so did John and Philip, and as they trudged along the dusty roads, that autumn day, they were glad to be going home.

Ever since they first met Jesus these five men had thought of nothing else but following Him, and listening to Him. Now for the first time they could introduce their families to Him, and bring Him into their houses.

Jesus walked a few steps ahead of them on the road, silent with His own thoughts. Behind Him the five friends talked earnestly in whispers.

"It will be good to get home," said Peter. "We have been away so long. I have almost forgotten what it is like to be a plain fisherman!"

"I wonder," said his brother Andrew, "what Jesus wants us to do. Remember we are all working men, used to working hard for a living with our boats and nets. Yet since we met Him we have done nothing but listen and learn, and walk the roads like vagabonds."

"Can He mean us to spend our lives like this?" asked Philip. "I will do whatever He says, for He is wiser than any man. And yet it seems strange to have idle hands, like a dreaming boy."

"He's a mystery to me," said Nathanael. "He believes hard work is good for a man, and something to be proud of. He was a carpenter Himself, remember. Yet He spends many hours dreaming Himself, and praying."

"Praying is work of a different kind," said John. "And preaching and teaching, too. We had better wait and see what He wants us to do. He will tell us, all in good time, whether we are to be fishermen, or not."

By then, the tree-lined streets of Capernaum lay ahead of them, and Peter's bearded face burst into a grin. He and his brother Andrew led Jesus proudly down by the waterfront, to their own house.

Peter was a widower. His wife had died several years before, and he and Andrew made their home with Peter's mother-in-law, a kindly old lady with hair the color of sea foam. She met them at the doorway and welcomed Jesus and His friends with a smile. She served them a warm drink to take away the chill of the autumn wind.

But privately she spoke to Peter, in a corner where no one else could hear:

"Peter, you have always taken good care of me. You have always worked hard. What has happened to you since you met this Jesus? True, we have enough money to live on. But your boat lies forgotten on the shore. Its seams are splitting, and you are not even here to fix it. Your nets are dry. You have not caught or sold a fish in months. And you do not even seem like your old self anymore. I'm worried about you, Peter," the old lady said. "And I'm not at all sure I approve of this Jesus of Nazareth."

Peter laid a big gnarled hand on her tiny shoulder, wondering what he could say. How could he tell her that Jesus was more important to him than work or home, more important than anything that ever happened to him?

"I wish you liked Him," Peter said. "Unless you love Him with your whole heart, you can never understand. But perhaps some day, you will. As for me, I must wait, and do only what He wants me to do. And I do not know yet what He wants of me."

Before the old lady could answer, Jesus and His

friends came forward to thank her, and make their goodbyes. The others were anxious to bring Him to their homes. He went to Philip's house, and then to the cottage where John lived. There Jesus met John's father, Zebedee, a grizzled old fisherman with a laugh sudden as thunder, and John's brother, James. This was the first time James had met Jesus, yet as he looked into the Master's dark eyes, James knew he too would follow wherever Jesus led.

The visits over, His disciples took Jesus on a walk through Capernaum, which was one of the most beautiful and famous cities in Palestine. They showed Him the hillsides where the brown nuts ripened on the trees, and purple figs grew fat and round on the branches. They took Him to see the synagogue, famous for its tall white Roman pillars. And then, laughing and singing, they led Him down to the shore of the Sea of Galilee, where they had lived and worked most of their lives.

Large dark-brown fishnets lay sprawled on the beach to dry, held down with little lead weights so that the wind should not blow them away. Here and there a man bent over the nets mending the holes so no fish could escape after it was caught. And Peter showed Jesus how the fish were pickled in barrels to be sold in far-away markets.

As they turned back from the beach, the disciples wondered, "Will we ever fish here again? When will He tell us what we are to do?"

Jesus stayed in Capernaum several days, teaching in the synagogue, and in the market place, and down by the shore, wherever people would listen to Him. Most of the time, His disciples were with Him, except for Peter, who was busy at home.

The day after Jesus arrived, Peter's mother-in-law had fallen ill of a dreadful fever. Her cheeks were flushed, her throat dry, her forehead burning. And Peter stayed home to watch over her.

Naturally, he called in a physician. This man, like other doctors of that time, looked very wise, and said very little, and used the strangest medicines ever imagined. He mixed his prescriptions out of such things as the heads of mice and the eyes of crabs, frogs' livers and elephant lice, or the ashes of a charred wolf's skull. To cure a cold he would tell his patient to kiss a mule on the nose! Frogs cooked in vinegar, he said, would take away a toothache!

For Peter's mother-in-law the doctor ordered rabbit ears and mouse fat, and a powder made of ground-up horse teeth. That medicine had helped others with the fever, but it did not help her.

One afternoon the fever grew worse and Peter grew alarmed, for by looking at her he could see she was close to death. He did not wait. He rushed out to the synagogue to fetch Jesus.

Andrew and Philip and Nathanael, James and John stood in the doorway watching as Jesus came in and went directly to the bed and touched the old lady's hand. She turned away from Him, then looked back at Him with bewildered eyes.

"The fever is gone!" she said. And she smiled. "I am well."

She was so well that she got out of bed and dressed and cooked dinner for all seven men and herself. Never again would she scold Peter for following this Man called Jesus!

By sunset the whole town heard about what Jesus had done, and Peter's house was mobbed. The narrow streets outside, the courtyard and the house itself were filled with sick people. They hobbled on crutches. Sons carried their sick old fathers on their shoulders. Mothers carried their feverish children in their arms. Some had pains and fevers, some were crippled and some were blind.

Upon them all, one after another, Jesus laid firm, cool hands. He blessed them with a smile, and sometimes even a chuckle for the youngsters. And each one he touched was cured. The blind could see His face, and the crippled could stand straight, and the fevers and the aches and the pains were gone.

Then Jesus explained that He could not stay longer in Capernaum. He must visit other cities around the Sea of Galilee. And this time He would go alone. But He promised to return, and until He came back His disciples should stay here, and go about their work as fishermen.

After Jesus left, the six men looked at each other.

"Perhaps that is our answer," said Peter. "Perhaps we are always to be plain fishermen. And yet somehow I do not think so."

"He said He would come back," said James, the brother of John.

"We'll wait and see. In the meantime—to work."

Down to the beach they went. With caulk and paint they fixed their boats. They mended their nets, and spread their sails. Long days they worked, and nights too, for night was often the best time of all to catch fish. But their luck was bad, and they caught few fish.

And then one day without warning Jesus returned. He stood on the shore teaching, and the crowd of listeners was so great that He was forced to move back to the very edge of the water. Nearby were two fishing boats with oars, mast, and sails. Fishermen stood in the water, washing their nets, but the baskets in which they kept their catch were empty.

Jesus saw that one of those boats belonged to Peter. He turned and climbed into the boat, asking Peter to pull it out a little further into the water. Using the boat as a stage, He finished His talk, safe from the impatient crowd on the shore.

When the crowd was gone, Jesus turned to His friend with a broad smile of welcome.

"Peter," He said, "take your boat out into the deep water and let your nets down to catch the fish."

Peter sighed. He wanted to be polite, but he must explain that that was a ridiculous idea. There were no fish to be caught, he was sure. And so he explained,

"We have fished all night—and have caught nothing!"

Jesus simply looked at Peter in silence.

"Well," said Peter, "if You say we should, we will."

So Peter called his helpers, and they sailed out into the sea, and let down their nets.

Then: "Look at the nets!" called one sailor.

"The nets are so full they'll break!" said Peter.

Through the water they could see the silver popping, wriggling, squirming fish, bulging the nets until the ropes broke. They had to call for help to their friends on another ship. They filled both ships with the catch, and even so the ships wobbled and nearly sank with the weight of the fish.

When they reached shore, Peter's face was red with shame, as he remembered how he had doubted what Jesus had said. He had even explained to Him that there were no fish! Unhappily he stood before Jesus now, and said in a low voice:

"Leave me—for I am a sinful man, O Lord!"

The others stood by watching—Andrew who was Peter's brother, and Philip, and the brothers James and John, and Nathanael. They heard Jesus answer:

"Come after Me, and I will make you fishers of men. Fear not!"

And He was speaking not only to Peter but to all of them. He had answered their question. He had called them to follow Him.

They left the boats with Zebedee, the father of James and John. And they started out, ready to follow Jesus all the way to the cross. Their hardest work lay ahead of them.

No more fishing—except as He told them, to catch the souls of men!

The Hole in the Roof

ALL around the Sea of Galilee Jesus and His first six disciples traveled, preaching and teaching. And everywhere Jesus went He turned His gentle dark eyes on those who were sick or in pain, and laid His strong cool hands on them and made them well. People saw His face, and they said:

"Never has there been such love in any face!"

And they knew without His having to tell them that He loved every person He saw, from the fat little baby in the cradle to the filthy old beggar asleep in the shadows. To each person He met, He offered a love deeper than anyone else can give, stronger than the love of mother or father, or wife, or husband, or friend.

To Him came the blind, and the deaf, people with hunchbacks and twisted legs, and He cured them all. More wonderful even than that, He cured the troubles no one could see, the nasty twisting troubles we call by other names, like hatred, and greed, and disobedience, and unhappiness.

No one could talk of anything else but the wonder of this Jesus. He was becoming famous, not only in Galilee, but all over Palestine.

Even in Jerusalem men had heard of this Man from Nazareth, and in the Temple the high priests heard of Him, and they began to worry. If He cured people, made the blind to see and the deaf hear, there was nothing wrong in that. But He was not only healing the sick, so they heard, but He was also teaching and preaching, just as if He were a high priest from the Temple too. If the Man were teaching the truth, all well and good—but what was He teaching to make so many people come and listen to Him?

Annas, the chief of all the Temple priests, called his most trusted spies.

"Go down among the crowds and listen to this Carpenter. And come and tell me what He is saying, for I think He is dangerous," said Annas.

Soon the spies from the Temple were following Jesus and His disciples from town to town, hiding in the crowds to watch and listen.

"It is amazing how many come to hear Him," whispered the spy with the drooping eye. "And yet I see nothing wrong."

"What He says sounds new and startling, and yet much of it comes straight from our own religious books. Only when He says it, and explains it, it sounds different," said the curly-haired spy.

"I think we have made this long trip for nothing," said the first. "Still, we'll wait and see."

That same afternoon, those spies began to feel they had indeed found a dangerous Man.

Jesus had come with His disciples into the house of a friend of His in Capernaum, and He sat in an upper room with some learned men of the town, answering their questions. The Temple spies were there too. They had orders to follow Him everywhere and miss nothing.

Suddenly overhead they all heard a rumbling and a scuffling, a noise as if the roof were going to fall in. The owner of the house, very annoyed, climbed to the roof, growling:

"Who is making all this racket?"

What he found there was a family, a wife and four sons, carrying a father who was deathly ill.

The wife on the roof pleaded with the angry house-

holder. "I know we shouldn't be on your roof, but listen—
please! My husband has a strange disease. He cannot move,
and he is in terrible pain. He cannot even move his lips to
speak or groan."

One of his sons spoke: "No doctor can cure him of this
paralysis so we have carried him to Capernaum to find Jesus.
But even here we could not get near Him. The people, the
crowds are so thick, and no one would let us through."

"So," said the wife, "we carried him and his bed
around here where there is no crowd, and up those steps to
the roof. We thought with these ropes we could let him down
on his bed through that wide window in the roof, and put
him right in front of the Master. And then, maybe He will
cure my husband."

And that was just what the family did. With ropes tied

to the corners of the light straw mattress they lowered the paralyzed father down to the Master's feet.

Jesus looked down at the unmoving man, and then up to the roof where staring down at Him were the tired mother and her sons. He smiled at them, then bent beside the dying stranger. Jesus placed His hands on the man's icy cheeks, and stroked his forehead. And then He spoke:

"Be of good heart, son! Your sins are forgiven you."

Everyone in the room gasped. The Temple spies sat up and their eyes were wide. Here was something to tell the high priest!

"That's a terrible thing to say!" squawked one. "Who can forgive sins but God alone? It's blasphemy to say that."

Jesus was still bending over the sick man. He faced the Temple spies. "What is it," He asked, "that you think in your hearts? Why do you think evil? Which is easier to say: 'Your sins are forgiven you'—or 'Arise! Take up your bed and walk?'"

He patted the cheeks of the man who could not move. Then Jesus whispered slowly and deliberately.

"But that you may know that the Son of Man has power to forgive sins, get up! I say to you, arise! Take your bed and go to your house."

Everything seemed to stand still for one breathless instant. Then in sight of all of them the man who could not move began to move. The man who could not speak spoke. The first sound was a great sob of relief, and joy that shook his whole thin wasted body. Struggling up to one elbow, he cried:

"Thanks be to God!"

Over his head his wife and four sons were crying with happiness. The man who had been sick pulled himself to his feet and stood swaying for a moment. Then he bent over and did as he had been told. He picked up his bed and walked out of the house.

And Jesus smilingly waved His hand in farewell to the wife and sons upstairs before they raced after the healed one.

The crowds were breaking up, jabbering and whispering and wondering. They too went chasing after the man with the bed to congratulate him.

Soon the only people left in the upper room were the Temple spies, and the scholars—they huddled in a corner and put their heads together.

"Whom did Jesus call Himself? The Son of Man?"

"What does that mean?"

"Ah!" One of them remembered. "Those words are in our Scriptures, in the Book of Daniel. Daniel said that the Son of Man would come to earth with the clouds of heaven."

"So—He pretends to be the Savior? That is a terrible thing for a man to say."

"It is worse for a man to say that he can forgive sins. Only God can forgive us for the wrong things we do!"

"And this Carpenter can't be God. We must hurry back to Jerusalem and tell Annas, the high priest, and the others in the Temple about this. They must stop Him."

"For a man to pretend he is God is blasphemy. And blasphemy is a crime punished by death."

The Temple spies scurried out of the house on their way back to Jerusalem with their report.

As they left, one learned man with a beard white as a waterfall, spoke:

"Still, He did cure the man with paralysis. And only one with the power of God can do that."

So it was that day, as on many others, that the men from the Temple did not believe Jesus. But the ordinary people, watching the wonders that He worked, did believe. And they understood that this was much more than a carpenter from Nazareth. This was indeed, the Son of Man and the Son of God.

The Wicked Queen

JOHN the Baptist, the cousin of Jesus of Nazareth, was in serious trouble.

John, the giant in animal skins and camel's-hair cloak, for months had been preaching to great crowds down by the Jordan River. He stood barefoot by the river, begging people to turn from sin and do only what was good and pleasing to God.

"Do penance!" he would shout. "The Kingdom of Heaven is at hand."

And John would name all the evil things that people were doing, and beg them to stop. No more fighting, or gossiping, or cheating. No more laziness, or selfishness. No more children disobeying their parents. No more lies. And he reminded them that all these things were insults to God.

But John the Baptist was not only scolding poor people for their sins. He wanted the whole world shining and clean and good, to be ready for the Savior. He wanted an end to all sin. And so John even dared to tell the world about the evil things that were done in the palace, and the sins of King Herod Antipas. King Herod had taken his brother's wife, Herodias, to live with him which was, of course, a sin. He even called her his Queen.

John the Baptist stood at the edge of the desert and thundered: "It is not lawful for him to have his brother's wife."

Now everyone knows it is a dangerous thing to say aloud that an important person like a king has done wrong, because often the most important people like to pretend that even the wicked things they do are all right for them.

King Herod, who thought himself important, grew angry when he heard the things John the Baptist was saying. But Queen Herodias, who thought she was even more important, and who was a very wicked woman in spite of her beautiful gowns and jewels, grew angrier still.

"Arrest that noisy fool called John," said the Queen. "Torture him, and whip him—and then put him to death! He cannot say such things about me!"

King Herod shook his head. "I will not put Him to death," he said, "because he is a good man. He has done nothing wrong."

But Herod knew he would have to do something to please Herodias, or she would be angry at him, too. So he sent his soldiers to seize John, and had him thrown into a dungeon in the darkest, slimiest cellars of the palace.

And then, in the secrecy of night, Herod would sneak down to the dungeon to talk with John the Baptist. Evil as the King was, he was fascinated by this man of the desert who was so good. John, who had nothing, seemed so happy, and the King, who had everything, was always so unhappy.

"Maybe," thought the King, "I can learn the secret of this happiness for myself."

But happiness is not an easy secret to learn. Each night when Herod came, John the Baptist tried to explain to him that to do wrong was to offend God, and that unless a man obeys God's laws he can never be happy. Happiness comes from goodness, said John.

"But it is too hard to be good," said the King, who was a very weak man. "There must be an easier way."

Meanwhile, even in his dungeon, John heard reports of all his cousin Jesus was doing and saying. He heard how

Jesus healed the rich man's son, and the man with paralysis. He heard how Jesus had cured a man with a withered hand, and driven devils out of an insane man in the synagogue.

He even heard the story of the time that Jesus made a dead man live again. He had been walking with His disciples down a street when a funeral procession came toward them. The only son of a widow had died, and they were carrying him to the cemetery to bury him. But Jesus stopped them, and went over and spoke to the dead young man, and took his hand—and the man had risen up, as alive as you or I!

While John was thinking about these strange and wonderful things, King Herod came again to see him.

"John," said the King, "do what I ask and I will set you free. Promise me to talk no more about sin and I'll let you go today. But if you refuse—if you insist on saying that my Queen and I are sinners—I shall have to have you beheaded. I have no choice. Herodias hates you so that she will make me kill you, John."

John shook his head with a smile. "Whether I live or whether I die, does not matter. But I cannot stop speaking about sin, because sin hurts God. And God is more important than any king."

John put his huge head close to the bars and spoke straight to the King who stood outside.

"And Herod—a great change is shaking the world even now. You should be ready. Now is the time to repent from sin. For the Messiah has come, the Savior. And I am sent to announce Him. I am His messenger," said John.

Herod burst into laughter, and all his double chins shook.

"For a fairy tale like that you would die?" asked the King. "Don't be a fool, John. All you need do to go free is to take back your nasty words about the Queen and myself.

But as to this Jesus—this Man from Nazareth, He is not God. *You* called Him that. But did *He* ever call Himself God? Did you ever hear Him say so? Couldn't you be wrong, John?"

John the Baptist thought for a moment. "I am sure that He is God. But—will you let me send some of my friends to ask Him? Then I will know what to do."

With the King's permission, John sent two men to Jesus in Galilee, to ask the most important question in John's life.

They said to Jesus: "Are you He that is come? Or must we look for another?"

Jesus said to them: "Go tell John what you have heard and seen. The blind see. The lame walk. The lepers are cured. The deaf hear. Those who are dead come back to life. And the gospel is preached to the poor!"

Two nights later Herod came again to the dungeon to look at John. "Well, Baptist," he said, "have your friends returned?"

"Yes, Majesty."

"Then you must have decided, John. Will you take back all those things you said and go free? Or will you insist on talking about sin—and die?"

"I must serve God, and do battle against sin. For Jesus—He is God come to earth."

Herod turned on his heel, and hurried angrily away. He could not look into those good clear eyes a moment longer, for all he saw in them was his own wickedness.

That same night, as it happened, a shining dinner party was being held in the palace. The night was hot and still, and the tall banquet hall was lit with torches and long tapers. The harpists and the drummers and the minstrels filled the night with music, and Herod's guests, a hundred or more, ate and drank their fill.

Near the end of the evening, as a special entertainment, Salome, daughter of Queen Herodias, came to dance for the guests. She was young and beautiful, and when she danced she seemed to weave a magic spell over all who watched her pale bare feet, and her drifting veils and robe.

When she finished, King Herod called her to him.

"Ask me whatever you want, Salome, and I will give it to you," he said, loud enough for the whole table to hear. "Whatever you ask, Salome, I'll give you—though it be half my kingdom!"

Salome turned and ran to her mother, the Queen, who waited in her room.

"Mother, Mother—what *shall* I ask for?" said Salome.

Wicked hatred burned in Herodias' eyes. "If you can have anything," she said, "ask for the head of John the Baptist! That man must die now."

Salome ran back to the banquet hall, back to the King.

"Well, Salome, what will it be?" asked Herod.

"I will that immediately you give me in a dish the head of John the Baptist."

Herod stared at Salome in horror. He had thought she would ask for gold and jewels, white horses and castles— never for such a thing as that! And yet, he had promised, in front of all his guests. Herod was not only wicked and sinful, he was a coward. He was afraid to say no.

In a quiet miserable voice, Herod called his servants.

"Fetch the executioner," he said. "Have him bring us here now the head of John called the Baptist. Bring it in a dish!"

The executioner hurried to the prison, and woke John, who lay peacefully asleep on the floor.

"Kneel—and lay your head on that block of wood!"

John knelt, and with one swing of an axe, the executioner cut off his head. He put the head on a golden dish, then carried it to Herod.

John's friends rode night and day till they reached Capernaum, and told the sad news to Jesus.

Alone through the night, Jesus went into the mountains, high over the Sea of Galilee to pray. John had been sent by God to prepare the way for Jesus. Now John's time was over. And Jesus must start His own work, the work of saving a sinful world.

The Chosen Twelve

WHEN Jesus chose His seventh disciple, He shocked everyone who knew Him. The first six of His friends were fishermen, poor men and uneducated, perhaps, but the kind of men all the people liked.

The seventh was a publican.

A publican was a special kind of tax-collector. His job was to sit at a booth on the highway, and stop every traveler and merchant who passed, and collect money from them. The money went straight to the Roman conquerors, whom everyone in Palestine hated. And because they hated the Romans, they loathed and despised anyone who worked for them.

So it was that the most unpopular man in Capernaum was the publican whose name was Levi. There was no personal reason for them to hate him. He was a good-natured fellow, and he had taken this job only because he was desperately poor, and needed to find work to earn a living. He sat at his booth on the highway, lonely and sad, while the village boys played tricks on him and no one scolded them.

"Robber!" they would yell at him as he walked down the street. "Thief!"

And Levi who was not a thief but an honest man, would bow his head and say nothing at all.

He worked hard and carefully, guarding the money he

104

had to collect for the Romans, keeping track of every mite and farthing and penny. And he was the loneliest man in town, for no one would be his friend.

One afternoon Levi sat at his booth, with a helper at his side, when Jesus of Nazareth came walking down the road. Jesus stopped at the booth, and looked into the sad eyes of the publican.

"Follow Me!" Jesus said suddenly.

Instantly the publican stood up. Not a moment's question. Levi, the despised, the friendless, rushed from his table. He called his assistant to take over the collection of the taxes, and without waiting for anything he fell in step and walked off briskly with the Master.

He was asked to follow—and he did it at once.

How proud he was to be with Peter and Andrew, James and John and Philip and Nathanael that afternoon. At last he had friends! Prouder still to be told by the Master he would no longer be called Levi, but would take a new name, the name of Matthew.

Matthew brought Jesus to his own house, the house to which no friend had ever come. He bustled out to the market to buy food, hardly counting the money he spent, only being certain he bought the best, for he was preparing a feast for the Master and His other disciples.

And when the feast was ready, Matthew hurried out to find guests to help him celebrate, and welcome Jesus. But the good men of Capernaum still would not come to Matthew's house, so the only guests he could find were others like himself, people no one wanted. Tramps. Beggars. The man who drank too much. The gamblers and the good-for-nothings of the town. These were the people Matthew brought to sit at table and break bread with Jesus, because the others were too proud to come.

The good people of the town came secretly in the moonlight, to peek through the windows and see for them-

selves that Jesus was eating with such a rag, tag, and bob-
tail crowd.

"Imagine! Eating with a publican—and with those aw-
ful people! That's no place for Jesus to be!" they said to
themselves.

When some of the disciples had finished supper, they
walked out into Matthew's garden for a breath of air. One
of the spies who had peered through the window grabbed
Peter's arm.

"Look here," he blustered. "Why does your Master
eat and drink with publicans and sinners, instead of with
good people, like us?"

The answer came at once, not from Peter, but from
Jesus Himself. Suddenly in the lighted doorway stood the
tall lean figure of the Teacher from Nazareth, calling to
them:

"Those who are well need no doctor—but those who are sick need him. Go, you, and learn this: I am not come to call the just, but sinners to repentance."

And the spies drifted off into the darkness. There was nothing for them to say. Jesus had said it all. He had come to save sinners, who needed Him far more than the people who are already good! And if the good are too proud to look for the Lord among the friendless and the poor and the sinners, they will find Him not at all.

It was only a few days later, when the news of the death of John the Baptist came that Jesus made the final choice of the men who were to be His disciples.

Some were already with Him, friends of every day. Others Jesus had chosen silently from the crowds that had followed Him for months wherever He went. Now He named those others, and sent Peter and James to fetch them. He gathered them all together on the pebbly shore of the Sea of Galilee, far away from the crowds.

Bald and bearded Peter with his freckled nose was there, of course, and his tall brother Andrew. Near them stood the pale Nathanael. Then came bright-eyed John, and his brother James, the fishermen sons of Zebedee. And standing beside them bearded Matthew, the publican. Philip, muscular and athletic, stood with one arm around Matthew's shoulder.

The others were all newcomers, strangers to the group.

First there was another, younger James, and his two brothers Jude Thaddeus and Simon Zelotes. Strange as it seems, these two were cousins of the Lord. Their mother was a grown-up sister of Mary, Jesus' mother. Not until this day did they come to work with Jesus, but for a long time He had been watching them, and He knew the goodness of their souls.

There was also one named Thomas, a bull-headed man with sturdy shoulders, the one we know today as doubting Thomas. And last of all stood a thin-faced, silent fellow, a little apart from the others—a man named Judas Iscariot.

Alone on the beach they stood, twelve men and God, while He told them what He wanted them to do.

Jesus told them He had chosen them as His messengers. He used the word "apostle," which in the language of that day meant "one who is sent," and they were all His apostles.

"Go you and preach," He said, "saying: the Kingdom of Heaven is at hand. Heal the sick, and raise the dead . . . And he that receives you, receives Me. And he that receives Me, receives Him that sent Me."

Carefully and in detail Jesus explained to these twelve men how difficult their job as apostles would be. He told them that they would be arrested, and beaten, and thrown into jail, and that men would hate them because they served Jesus. He told them of all the dangers and sorrows that waited for them.

And He told them too that they should have no fear, for God would watch over them, and protect them, and bring them one day to heaven.

The twelve apostles listened in silence.

Their lives had changed so completely, so quickly. Only a short time before they had been busy with the little things of everyday life—with earning a living, and buying and selling, and worrying about the weather. And suddenly Jesus had chosen them. And now they were to be messengers of God—teaching and preaching, even healing the sick as Jesus did. Now they were to face even death for the sake of their Master—all because God had chosen them as His own.

Other people would think that Jesus of Nazareth had chosen very strange friends.

"A bunch of dumb fishermen, that's what most of them are. And a publican. What kind of apostles are those?" they asked.

But God often chooses the people others would leave behind, and with His help and grace the dullest and the ugliest and the dumbest of us all can become apostles, serving Him today. Anyone—a freckle-nosed fisherman from Galilee, or a pug-nosed child from a modern city—can become truly great just by giving his heart to the Lord completely.

For that was the secret of the twelve apostles. They had given their hearts to Jesus of Nazareth, completely.

The Sermon on the Mount

TWELVE men sat on a mountainside, alone with Jesus. Twelve men who loved Him, and had promised to follow Him, sat in the afternoon sunlight and learned for the first time what it meant to be a Christian. "Come! Follow Me!" Jesus had said.

They had followed Him into Peter's gray fishing boat, and sailed with Him across the green waters of the Sea of Galilee. At His order they beached the boat on a lonely part of the shore, under the shadow of a towering mountain of black volcanic rock. Up the steep path they climbed till they reached a windflower-lined ledge overlooking the inland sea. Below them the late afternoon fog began to mist over the waters. Over their heads hung the blue sky. It was as though they were on an island of rock, floating between earth and heaven, alone with the Son of God.

An hour before, Jesus had officially chosen these men to be His apostles—messengers, teachers, and soldiers of faith. He had picked them to be the first Christians. And He had brought them to this mountainside to explain what this new faith was, to show them the glories and the hardships, the shining wonders and heavenly mysteries that were to be theirs—and ours.

There on the sunlit ledge He told them all that a soul needs to know of God and the world He has made, of to-day, and the life to come.

And Jesus was speaking not only to the men who were

110

to be His apostles, but to you, and to me. He was explaining exactly how we should live to please God, whether we are fishermen in Galilee, or businessmen, or children, in this century or the next. The men who heard Him on that afternoon learned His words by heart, and wrote them down for all to read, and treasure. Never have those words been forgotten, though often they are misunderstood.

What does it mean to be a Christian? It means first of all to live in happiness.

Ever since the world was born people have searched for happiness without finding it. They have said: If I had more money, or more of the things money can buy, then I would be happy. They tell themselves that if only they were older, or younger, or stronger, or more beautiful, then certainly they would be happy. And they are wrong. Happiness is found not in getting, but in giving, and in loving God, and following His laws.

Jesus came to offer us happiness. He did not say that we would ever escape pain, or tears, or sickness, or poverty. But He promised that in spite of all those things we could still be happy, and blessed, if we lived as Christians should.

What must we do to be truly happy?

Sitting on the grass, with the soft twilight wind in His hair, Jesus answered that question for His apostles, and for us. He gave us eight rules, which were to be called the Beatitudes, because those who live by them are blessed. And because the One who spoke those rules was the Son of God unchanging, they are as true today as when He spoke on that mountainside so long ago.

"Blessed are the poor in spirit, for theirs is the kingdom of heaven," said Jesus, in His deepest, gentlest voice.

And He meant: Happy are the people who are humble and not proud, who do not boast and brag. A good

Christian, He was saying, does not care about riches or fame, or proving how wonderful he is, because he knows that God is more wonderful than anything on this earth.

"Blessed are the meek, for they shall possess the land," said Jesus.

And He meant: If you accept God's will, and believe that because He is good everything He does is good, you will find true happiness. Then nothing that happens to you can frighten you, or make you feel forsaken and alone. A good Christian, He was saying, knows that God loves him, and cares for him, and he feels safe even in the face of darkness and trouble.

"Blessed are they that mourn, for they shall be comforted," said Jesus.

And He meant: You who weep and sorrow for others who are in trouble, and you who help those in need, shall find happiness.

"Blessed are they that hunger and thirst after justice, for they shall have their fill," said Jesus.

And He meant: You who really want to know God, and to know how to serve Him, will surely find happiness, for God will show you His ways, and feed your soul with His love.

"Blessed are the merciful," said Jesus, "for they shall obtain mercy.

"Blessed are the clean of heart—for they shall see God.

"Blessed are the peacemakers, for they shall be called the children of God."

Jesus paused and looked at the twelve men who sat in a circle before Him, men who would soon be killed simply because they served Him. He was about to tell them a startling secret—they would find happiness in suffering, and even in dying for His sake. We may never have to die as they did, but every one of us who are Christians at some time in our lives will suffer a bit for His sake, and His words are true for us as they were for those twelve apostles.

"Blessed are they that suffer persecution for justice's sake, for theirs is the kingdom of heaven.

"Blessed are you when they shall revile you and persecute you, and speak all that is evil against you, untruly, for My sake. Be glad and rejoice, for your reward is very great in heaven!"

The twelve men sat in silence, caught between the gray fog below and the golden light of sunset above. In their hearts His words repeated themselves over, and over—the eight rules of Christian life, so difficult, so simple, so full of the promise of blessed happiness.

Then Jesus spoke again.

Did they remember the Ten Commandments, the laws which God had given Moses so long ago? They did. Then, said Jesus, remember that those laws are important for all Christians, too. But it is not enough to keep from doing evil things, a Christian must not think evil either. And a Christian must be full of love, and kindness, even when it is hardest to love and be kind. To be angry is a sin. To call another a fool, is a sin.

"You have heard it said," Jesus asked, "that you shall love your neighbor and hate your enemy?"

The twelve men nodded. Of course!

Jesus shook His head. "But I say to you: Love your enemies!"

Gently He went on: "Do good to them that hate you. And pray for them that persecute you, and say evil things about you. Remember that you are the children of your Father Who is in heaven, Who makes His sun to rise upon the good, and bad—and His rain to fall upon the just and the unjust."

Quietly, solemnly, He said:

"Be you perfect, as also your heavenly Father is perfect."

Be perfect, He said, but never boast of your perfection.

As the setting sun painted the gray mountain rock with gold and rose light, Jesus explained that a Christian must never be a show-off, especially about his good deeds. If you brag about how kind and generous and loving you are, to make other people admire you, that will be your reward. But if you try to hide your goodness from everyone except God, your reward will come from Him. And, after all, nothing you can find on earth is worth one drop of what you will find in heaven, because the only reason God has created us, and the world we live in, is to let us prepare for a life with Him forever in heaven.

Money? Riches?

Jesus, the King of Heaven who was born in a stable cave, spoke through the twilight:

"Lay not up for yourselves treasures on earth—where rust and moths can consume them, and where thieves break through and steal. But lay up to yourselves treasures in heaven—where neither the rust nor moth can consume, and where thieves do not break through, nor steal.

"For where your treasure is, there is your heart also."

He raised His eyes till He looked far over the heads of His twelve, far over the darkening sea.

"No man can serve two masters. . . . You cannot serve God, and the world with its riches.

"Therefore I say to you, do not think it is important to worry about how you shall find food to eat so that you may live, or how you shall find fine clothes to wear. Is not life more than meat? And the body more than clothes?

"Behold the birds of the air. They do not sow seed, nor reap a harvest, nor gather food into barns. And your heavenly Father feeds them. Are not you of much more value

than they? And which of you, by worrying about it, can make yourself even eighteen inches taller?

"And why should you worry about clothing?"

Jesus bent over and touched a brilliant flower growing in the ledge. "Consider the lilies of the field, how they grow. They do not work. They do not spin cloth. But I say to you, that not even King Solomon in all his glory, was dressed as beautifully as one of these. And if God clothes the grass of the field in such glory, how much more richly will He care for you?

"Be not worried, then, saying: What shall we eat? Or what shall we drink? Or with what will we be clothed? Your Father knows you need these things.

"Seek first the kingdom of God, and His justice—and all these things shall be given to you, too."

Jesus rose to His feet, and His tall figure stood out black against the purple evening sky. The last glow of the sunset crowned His hair with golden light, as He spoke the most wonderful promise of all time, the promise that God will answer every prayer.

"Ask—and it shall be given to you.

"Seek, and you shall find.

"Knock, and it shall be opened to you. For every one that asks, receives. And he that seeks, finds. And to him that knocks, it shall be opened.

"Which man is there among you, who, if his son asks him for bread, would give him a stone? Or if his son asks for a fish to eat, would he give him a serpent?

"If you, who are evil, know how to give good gifts to your children—how much more will your Father Who is in heaven give good things to them that ask Him?"

And now, as darkness settled around them, and night had come, Jesus told His twelve a story. For Jesus was all-wise, and He knew that men remember stories, and understand what they mean, longer than they remember plain words.

"Everyone that hears My words, and obeys them," said Jesus, "is like a wise man who built his house on a rock. And the rain fell and the floods came and the winds blew and they beat upon that house. But that house did not fall, because it was built on a rock.

"And everyone who hears these words of Mine, and does not follow them, shall be like a foolish man that built his house upon the sand. And the rain fell, and the floods came, and the winds blew, and they beat upon that house, and it fell—and great was the fall of it!"

All these things and more Jesus explained to the Twelve as they sat around Him on the mountainside. The stars shone in the sky, and a little crescent moon began to rise as He told them that only by prayers could a man find the strength to live a life like that.

And how should a Christian pray? He should remember that God is his Father and knows what he needs even before he asks. And he should pray like this:

"Our Father, Who art in heaven, hallowed be Thy name. Thy kingdom come. Thy will be done, on earth as it is in heaven. Give us this day our daily bread. And forgive us our trespasses as we forgive those who trespass against us. And lead us not into temptation, but deliver us from evil . . ."

And the twelve disciples prayed with Him, and the stars shone bright overhead as they learned for the first time the prayer we call the Lord's Prayer.

And that was the Sermon on the Mount, as it was written down for us by Matthew, who had been a publican, but whom we call St. Matthew.

The First Box of Ointment

JESUS was invited to dinner in the home of a Pharisee named Simon.

In those days a Pharisee was a man who thought that God approved of him much more than of anyone else. The word Pharisee in the language they spoke then meant "someone who is separate from everyone else." The Pharisees had made a list of hundreds of little rules which they said had to be obeyed to please God, but inside themselves they had no love for God or for anyone but themselves. They were almost all very rich, and powerful, and they were also very greedy, and very proud.

Now Jesus of course did not approve of people like the Pharisees. Many of the people who lived in those times were afraid of the Pharisees, but Jesus had no fear of any man, no matter how rich or powerful. And Jesus, speaking to the crowds, told them exactly what He thought of the Pharisees.

He called them hypocrites, men who pretend to be so good and so holy, and secretly are full of evil and wickedness. And He said:

"Woe to you scribes, and Pharisees, hypocrites! Because you are like white marble tombs, which on the outside seem to be beautiful, but inside are full of dead men's bones, and of all filthiness!"

Naturally, the Pharisees did not like it when Jesus said such things about them!

At first they decided to pay no attention to Him. And then, when He kept on telling the crowds how wicked they were, the Pharisees decided the thing to do was to laugh it off as a joke.

"After all," they said, "who is going to believe what a crazy Carpenter from Nazareth has to say about us? We are too rich and too important to care what this Jesus says!"

But finally they realized that even if they thought Jesus was just a crazy carpenter, the good people who heard Him knew He was much more than a carpenter, and believed what He said. Finally the Pharisees in the town of Capernaum talked it over, and decided they had better find out more about Jesus.

One of them, a rich man named Simon, said: "I will invite Him to dinner and talk to Him myself, and see what kind of fellow He is. Maybe if He meets me, and sees what a wonderful man I am, He will stop saying these things about us. Maybe if I offer Him some money He will stop, too. It could be only because He is poor and jealous of us that He says such terrible things!"

Which only showed how little Simon understood about Jesus!

Simon sent his servant to invite Jesus to have dinner with him. But when the twelve apostles heard about the invitation, they tried to stop Him from going.

"Simon is a wicked man. He did not really earn the money that has made him rich," said Peter, who had lived in Capernaum all his life and knew a great deal about this Simon. "He cheats and steals to get his money. He sells sugar, and mixes sand with it. He sells horses that look strong and well, and are really sick and old. He is no one for You to eat with!"

"Simon is proud, and cruel. He goes and prays in public where everyone will see him and think he is holy, but in secret he laughs at the very idea of God. He makes a big fuss about giving a few coins to the poor, but truth is a stranger to his lips," said Andrew, Peter's brother.

But Jesus only smiled. He Who knows every secret of each person who has ever lived knew exactly why Simon invited Him, and He knew, too, just what sort of person Simon was. And still, He went to dinner.

Now in those days there were certain things which men did when guests came to their house, things which sound strange to us, perhaps, but were part of good manners and courtesy. When a guest came, for example, the host always offered a basin of water, and a towel, to wash the dust of the roads from his feet. The host always kissed the guest to show him he was welcome.

When Jesus came to Simon's house, Simon offered Him no water for His feet, and gave Him no kiss. And Simon had invited no other guests, which in the custom of the region was an insult. He did not serve his best meats, nor his strong oriental brandy. Clearly the rich Simon did not think any carpenter from Nazareth deserved the same courtesy he would show his own friends.

Jesus pretended not to notice. He sat down at the table with a cheerful smile. The two ate of boiled rice, raisins, spice, and lamb meat, and talked of the small things of which any two men might talk—of the weather, and the news of war in the west, and of the crops, and the taxes.

Suddenly Simon leaned forward, glaring over the shoulder of Jesus. Behind Him stood a woman with long red hair, wearing a scarlet robe of perfumed silk. In her hands she was holding an alabaster box.

Simon knew who she was. All of Capernaum knew her, for she was a wicked and famous woman, and no decent person would have anything to do with her.

The red-haired woman did not even look at Simon. She knew the Pharisee would send her out of his house. With tears in her eyes she looked only at Jesus.

She knelt beside Him, and washed His feet with her own hands, and her tears fell like rain. She wiped the calloused, journey-hardened soles with her long red hair, and tenderly kissed the insteps. Then she rubbed those feet with ointment from her box of alabaster.

The Pharisee sat back thinking to himself:

"There, you see! This Man, if He were really holy, and a prophet or a messenger of God, He would surely know who this woman is, and how wicked she is, and He would tell her to go away. Wait till I tell the world about this!"

Then Jesus said softly:

"Simon, I have something to say to you."

"Say it."

"Two people owed one man some money. One owed him five hundred pence and the other fifty."

"Yes?"

"Neither one could pay what they owed, and so he forgave them both."

"Yes?"

"Which of the two loves him more?"

"I suppose," said Simon, "the one to whom he forgave the most."

"You are right. Do you see this woman? I entered your house. You gave Me no water for My feet, but she has washed My feet with her tears, and with her hair has wiped them. You gave Me no kiss, but since she came in she has not stopped kissing My feet.

"Many sins are forgiven her," said Jesus, "because she has loved much."

And for the first time Jesus spoke to the red-haired Mary Magdalene and said: "Your sins are forgiven you."

"Who are You to forgive sins?" snarled Simon, jumping to his feet.

But Jesus was paying no attention to His host. He helped the red-haired woman to her feet and gently closed the lid of her box of alabaster. Expensive that box was, and the ointment was even more expensive. All her savings must have gone to buy it.

And He said to her:

"Your faith has made you safe. Go in peace!"

And immediately afterward He, too, left the rich man's house.

"The Man is crazy," said Simon to himself. "And dangerous."

He did not understand the lesson Jesus had tried to teach him. He did not understand that because Jesus loves us He can forgive even the worst of us, if we will only love Him. The red-haired woman wept because she knew she had done many wrong things that offended God—and Jesus forgave her. But Simon was proud, and he liked to think he was perfect, and did not have any sins to be forgiven.

So it was on that night that Jesus walked out of his house, and Simon was left alone.

The Story of the Prodigal Son

THE blue waters of the Sea of Galilee sparkled in the sunlight, and the winds whispered over the shell-strewn shore. In a boat by the beach stood Jesus, leaning on the prow as if it were a pulpit. And on the sand, and the slopes of grass, and even in the branches of the trees above, the crowds sat and listened to Him speak.

The men had left their hammers and their pens and ink, their shops and their farms, to listen. The women had left their dusting and sweeping, and brought their children, to hear Him. They came because they knew He was speaking great truths, and because when He spoke of God, and the mysteries of heaven, they could understand.

Jesus was the greatest teller of good stories the world has ever heard, and the stories He told are called parables. Jesus knew that no one's mind is big enough to understand the God who made us, and so He put God's secrets into stories which we can understand and remember.

The one parable of Jesus that the people remembered best was the adventure of the prodigal son, which means as you know, the son who was wasteful, and threw his money away.

Jesus stood in the swaying bow of the ship, and His eyes twinkled as He began the story.

"A certain man had two sons. . . ."

He was a rich man, this father, who had worked hard

to make his farm the finest in the country. He had many acres of land, on which grew good purple grapes, and tall ears of corn, and wheat, and oats and barley. He had fine sleek horses, and big brown-and-white cows to give milk and butter and cheese, white lambs, and a busy flock of chickens. And he had many servants in his house, and hired men in the fields.

Now this rich man had planned that when he died his two sons would inherit the farm and all his money, half for each of them. But the younger son, whom we may call Jacob, did not want to wait. The farm bored him, and he thought that if only he had some money now, and went to the big city, then he could be happy. So he went to his father and said:

"Father, give me my share of the money that will be mine. But give it to me now, while I am still young. I do not want to wait later. And I don't want to stay on this farm all my life!"

The father pulled thoughtfully at his beard, and his gray eyes grew very sad. Ever since his son was a boy he had tried to teach him the good way to live. He had tried to teach him to love God and serve Him, and to be kind and good and wise. And he had tried to make him see that hard work was not only important, but a thing to be proud of, and to enjoy. He had taught his son as best he could, and now his son was a man, and must think for himself, and decide.

"My son would be happier here than in the city, I know," he said to himself. "But if I tell him that he will think I am old and grumpy, and do not understand him. And if I refuse to give him the money, and make him stay here, he will not love me or the farm any better. The only thing to do is let him lead his own life and make his own decisions— and pray that he does not come to harm."

So the father drew out of his chests the money his son asked for, and gave it to him. And a few days later, the son packed his things, and said goodbye to his father and to his brother, and went abroad into a far country to see the world. And as he left the farm he did not even look back to notice the tears in his father's eyes.

"I shall never go back," said the prodigal son. "I'll not be stuck on the farm, working and worrying about sun and rain and drought, the way my father does. Why should I work anyway? I have money. Only stupid fools would work when they already have money. I'm going to spend mine, and have a good time."

So Jacob went abroad with his purse full of gold and silver, and he expected that before long he would become a very great fellow. He was sure that his money would bring him friends and power and even more money, and soon he would be living like a king.

But Jacob was not very wise in the ways of the city. And the wicked men of the city heard the jingle of his purse and rubbed their hands together with glee as they schemed and planned to get the money away from him.

They smiled at Jacob, and put their arms around his shoulders and laughed at his jokes, and pretended to be his friends. They taught him to drink wine, more, far more, than was good for him, and when he had drunk too much and did not know what he was doing, they stole some of his gold.

They taught him how to gamble, and bet large sums of money on a throw of dice or the fall of a card. And because they smiled and winked while they played with him, he never guessed that they were cheating him.

They promised to help him meet all the rich and important people of the city. They told him to give great parties, and they would bring the famous people as guests. So he spent his money on food and wines for the parties, on dancing girls and musicians—but his only guests were the same wicked men and their friends, who were neither rich nor important at all.

In a few months, Jacob's money was all spent. His purse was empty. And when he went to the inns and taverns to find the men who had said they were his friends, they turned their backs on him, and pointed fingers at him and laughed.

A famine came on the land where Jacob was, and all the crops were ruined by bad weather, and there was little food for anyone—especially for a man who had no money and no job. Jacob grew hungry. He walked the streets of the city looking for a job, but no one would hire him.

"What good are you?" laughed the merchants and the shopkeepers and the innkeepers. "What do you know of city life, of buying or selling, or of keeping books? Go back to the country!"

Jacob was weak with hunger, and his cheeks were pale and sunken. His fine city clothes, for which he had spent so much money, were tattered and ragged, and he had to sleep in the streets, or huddled on the steps of a building, because he could not pay for a place to live.

Finally Jacob walked out into the countryside looking for work there. He stopped at the first farm he came to, and knocked at the door.

"Have you any work that I could do?" he asked the farmer. "I am poor, and hungry, but I will take any job."

The farmer looked at the young man and frowned.

"You don't look like you'd be good for much of anything," he said. "But I'll put you to work. You can take care of the pigs—and live with them."

Jacob was so hungry that he took the job, and dirtier, more disgusting work than caring for those swine would be hard to find. He was so hungry that he ate some of the husks

which were meant for the pigs' food, because no one would give him anything to eat.

That night, as he made himself a bed of straw in the corner by the pig pen, Jacob never felt lonelier, or closer to tears, even though he was a full-grown man. Alone with the grunting, smelling hogs, he thought to himself:

"Even the hired servants in my father's house have plenty to eat, and here I am nearly dying with hunger. I know that I have been a bad son, and do not even deserve to be called his son any more. But still—I will go to my father and say to him:

"Father, I have sinned against heaven and before you. I have wasted my money, and done many wicked things, and I have been a fool. But even though I am not worthy to be part of your family, will you take me back as one of your servants? For I can learn to work!"

And Jacob got up from his muddy bed, and set off through the night. For more than a week he walked, begging food as he went, and drinking water from the streams, and sleeping in the cold with no blanket under the trees.

Finally he came within sight of his father's farm—and now, what is that that he sees ahead? A hurrying figure coming toward him through the dust!

From far off his father had seen him coming, and ran to greet him, and running to him put his arms around him and kissed him.

"Father," said the prodigal son, "I am sorry. I do not even deserve to be called your son."

The father turned to his servants. "Go quickly and bring a fine robe and put it on him to cover his cold bones, and put a ring on his hand, and shoes on his feet. And go and kill the fatted calf, and roast it. Let us eat and make merry, because this my son was dead to me, and he has come to life again—he was lost and is found!"

Now the older son was out in the fields working, and

when he came back to the house he heard music and dancing.

"There is a great feast, because your brother has come home," one of the servants told him.

And when the older son heard that he was so angry he would not even go into the house. His father came out to ask him to join the celebration, but he said to his father:

"This isn't fair. I have served you for years, and obeyed you, and worked hard. And I have never done anything wrong. But you never gave me a feast. Yet look—Jacob goes off and wastes his money gambling and drinking and for him you kill the fatted calf."

His father put his arms around him and held him close. "Son," he said, "you are always with me, and all I have is yours. You know that I love you.

"But your brother who was lost is found, and has turned from his evil ways, and has been saved for us. It is only right that we should rejoice."

And the father and the older son went in and welcomed Jacob, and rejoiced.

And, said Jesus, to His listeners on the beach, God is a Father like that—and we are His children. If we turn from Him, and leave His ways, we will suffer just as did the prodigal son. But like that son, no matter how wicked we have been, we need only to be sorry, and to come back again to God's house, and He will welcome us, and comfort us, and warm us with His love.

God, said Jesus, is a Father, waiting for all His sons to come home.

The Story of the Good Samaritan

WHAT kind of Man is this Jesus?" snorted a haughty-faced man by the roadside. "He looks like a vagabond, a plain ordinary tramp. Why, He and His apostles spend most of their time walking the highways. If He were as great a teacher as men say, why wouldn't He stay put, and let people come to Him?"

And indeed Jesus and His apostles were not impressive to look at. Their robes were dusty and their feet were calloused and hard, as they trudged along the road.

"Why does your Master travel so much?" asked the man.

Peter answered: "He goes to teach the people, to bring His message to those who cannot come to Him. Our Master is not too proud to go to the poorest house, or the farthest town. Men may be too busy to come to Him, but He is never too busy to come to them!"

On that day in November, when the ruts in the road were frozen hard as carved wood, Jesus led His apostles to a small town called Bethany, in Judea. There they stopped at the home of three old friends of the family, two sisters named Martha and Mary, and Lazarus their brother. And, as He often did, Jesus went to preach in the town synagogue.

The congregation crowded the little house of worship that morning, to hear the words of this famous teacher named Jesus. And as they listened Jesus told them that He promised eternal life to all good people in this world. And what did He mean by eternal life? He meant that even after they died, and their bodies were buried, they would live with God forever in heaven. That was eternal life.

When Jesus said that, everyone was silent wondering. What kind of person was this Who dared to promise eternal life? For they did not know, because He had not told them, that Jesus was the Son of God.

Then one man stood up. He was a lawyer, and he knew the laws of the Scripture by heart. Perhaps, he thought, I can catch this Jesus in a mistake, for He does not look like a man who has studied anywhere near as much as I have!

With a sly look in his left eye, the lawyer said ever so politely: "Master, what must I do to possess eternal life?"

Jesus knew what was in the lawyer's heart. And so He said: "What is written in the law? How do you read it?"

The lawyer blinked. "The law says: You shall love the Lord your God with your whole heart, and with your whole soul, and with all your strength and with all your mind. And you shall love your neighbor as yourself."

And Jesus said: "You have answered rightly. Do this, and you shall live."

But the lawyer did not sit down. "But who *is* my neighbor?" he demanded. "Just which people do I have to love to win eternal life?"

And when he asked that question, the lawyer was hoping to trap Jesus. Because the men to whom Jesus was talking were born Jews, just as Jesus was. And no Jew would have anything to do with the people called Gentiles—or the even worse people called Samaritans.

The lawyer had heard that Jesus had once visited the Samaritans, and eaten with them, and even preached to them. Would He say that even Samaritans were neighbors? That to win eternal life one had to love even such terrible people?

"Master," asked the lawyer raising his eyebrows, "who is my neighbor?"

From where Jesus sat, He could look down the aisle and through the open door to the road beyond, the road that led from Jericho to Jerusalem. That highway was famous as the hiding-place of robbers and thieves, a dangerous place for any traveler. Jesus gazed out at the road, and in answer to the lawyer He began to tell a story, a parable that has never been forgotten.

"*A certain man went down from Jerusalem to Jericho and fell among robbers———*" Jesus began.

And the men listening could see it all in their imaginations as He spoke. They could see that "certain man" packing his bags for the journey, his worried wife helping him and begging him not to go alone, but to wait till he could get someone to go with him. No, no—the business was urgent. He must get to Jericho before dawn tomorrow.

Then his ten-year-old son came to him:

"I know someone going on that road tonight—my friend's father. Why not go with him? He comes from Nablus, and he is a Samaritan, and ———"

"What?" roared the father. "What is a son of mine doing playing with a Samaritan boy? Don't you know that no decent person has anything to do with Samaritans?"

"What's wrong with Samaritans, Father?" asked the boy. "My friend is very nice."

"Listen, son," said the father. "Samaritans are all dirty, and they cannot be trusted. Hundreds of years ago they———"

"But Father, what does something that happened hundreds of years ago mean to us? My friend wasn't even alive then!"

"That's enough!" the father said sharply. "No more Samaritan friends for you. No son of mine may be seen playing with a Samaritan. Do you understand that? And tonight I shall go alone to Jericho."

The father started out on the dark road, alone, and

when he was far from town thieves overtook him, and took not only his money, but all his clothes. They left him naked on the ground in the dark—beaten, wounded, and half dead.

And now the crowd was very still as Jesus told them:

"And it chanced that a certain priest went down the same way, and saw him, and passed by.

"And in the same way a Levite when he was near the place and saw him, passed by.

"But a certain Samaritan, being on his journey, came near him, and seeing him took pity on him."

And the Samaritan did not pass by. He knew it was dangerous to stop on the road for anything, and he too was in a hurry just as the others had been. But still, he stopped.

He went over to the wounded man, and bandaged him, pouring oil and wine into the deep cuts left by the robbers' knives, and tying them up with clean strips of cloth. Then he picked the man up, and put him on his own horse, and brought him to an inn, and took care of him.

And the next day, when the Samaritan had to leave, the wounded man was still not well enough to travel. So the Samaritan took money out of his own purse and gave it to the innkeeper, and said:

"Take care of him, and whatever more you may need to spend, I will repay you when I return."

And without even waiting for thanks the Samaritan went on his way.

Jesus paused and looked from the faces of the people straight at the lawyer.

"Which of these three men—the priest, the Levite, or the Samaritan—was a neighbor to the man that fell among the robbers?"

And looking back into the smiling face of the Master the lawyer could answer only:

"He that showed mercy to him." And he meant, the Samaritan.

And Jesus said to him: "*Go, and do you in like manner!*"

The men and women of Bethany never forgot the story of the Good Samaritan. And even today, wherever it is told, men remember that when God says He wants us to love our neighbors He means for us to love everyone, and hate and despise no one.

The Daughter of Jairus

THE man named Jairus paced up and down the marble floor of the downstairs room of his house.

"Are the doctors still in there?" he asked in a voice so low it could hardly be heard over the sound of his sandals. "Will they never come out and tell me how Joanna is?"

His friend put an arm on Jairus' shoulder. "Jairus, sit down and rest. Since your daughter became ill you have not rested. The doctors are trying their best to make her well. And you must wait, and have patience, and take care of yourself. What else can you do?"

Jairus raised tear-stained eyes to meet his friend's gaze.

"My little girl is sick, dangerously sick, and you ask me what I can do? I can get her the best doctors—and that I have done. And because I am head of the synagogue, and love my God, I can pray. I have prayed night and day that He would make her well. And if doctors and prayers do not work, I know what I shall do."

"What more can you do, Jairus?"

"I shall go to Jesus, and ask Him to save her," said Jairus.

His friend's eyes opened wide with surprise. "Do you, the head of the synagogue, such a wise and important person as you, believe in this Jesus of Nazareth?"

"I do," said Jairus. "He has helped many. Perhaps He will help Joanna. And why should it surprise you that I believe in Him? He is wiser, and far more important than I, and He speaks with surer knowledge than I."

"Men will call you foolish to go to Jesus—a carpenter turned preacher, a poor Man who wanders the roads like a vagabond!" said his friend. "Don't go to Him!"

Slow footsteps echoed on the stairs. Jairus turned as the three doctors came into the room, carrying their scarlet and green bags of medicines and powders. The oldest doctor, whose face was gray and wrinkled as desert rock, put his hands on Jairus' shoulders.

"Jairus, there is nothing more that we can do. Your daughter—Joanna is dying."

Jairus stared at the doctor, and his cheeks went pale. Then without a word, he shook off the doctor's hands, and ran out of the house.

"Where has he gone?" asked the doctor.

"He has gone to see the One called Jesus," said his friend.

"Fool!" said the doctor. "What can Jesus do that we cannot?"

"Have you seen Jesus?" asked Jairus of the washer-woman by the town well.

"He is down by the shore," the woman said. "I'm on my way there soon."

But Jairus could not wait. He ran through the streets and down the hills, his sandals flapping, and his brown and orange robes streaming out in the breeze. And as he ran he thought of Joanna, the little girl he loved so dearly, the twelve-year-old with the black eyes who liked to sing and to play house under the tree in the back yard. Why would God want her to die? What possible reason could there be for a pink-cheeked little girl to die?

At last Jairus reached the beach. A thick crowd sur-rounded Jesus, but Jairus pushed and pleaded and squirmed his way through, and when he saw the Master, Jairus fell on his knees by Jesus' feet.

"My daughter is at the point of death," he said. "Come —and just lay Your hand on her—and then she will be safe, and will live. Please, Lord—come."

With His strong hands Jesus helped Jairus to stand, and rose Himself to go with him to his house. But the crowds followed Him through the streets, pushing and jostling and elbowing each other to get closer to Jesus. And there was in the crowd a woman who had been sick for twelve years, with a wound that never stopped bleeding. And she said to herself, "If I can only get close enough to touch Jesus' robe, that alone would make me well." Sick as she was, she made her way through the crowd.

Suddenly Jesus stopped. "Who touched Me?" He asked.

The apostles looked at Him and laughed. "Is this some kind of joke, Master?" asked Philip. "Look at the crowds all around you. How can You ask which person touched You?"

But Jesus did not even smile. He turned and looked behind Him, and from out of the crowd came the woman, and kneeling before Him she said:

"Lord, I touched Your robe, and I knew if I did, You could heal me. And see, I am made well again!"

Jesus put a hand in blessing on her head. "Daughter," He said, "it is your faith that has made you well. Go in peace."

Jairus stood silent beside Jesus. He did not dare say anything, but to himself he was thinking: Why, oh why, must He heal this woman now? If we don't hurry it will be too late to save Joanna!

And then Jairus saw his friend and the doctors shouldering their way through the crowd.

"Jairus," said his friend. "Your daughter is dead. Why trouble the Master any more? It is too late, now."

But Jesus heard what the man had said, and He turned

to Jairus, and put His arm around him. And Jesus whispered:

"Fear not. Only—*believe!*"

And with His arm firmly around Jairus, Jesus walked with him up the streets until they came to Jairus' house. A crowd came with them—but there was already another large throng at the house. All Jairus' relatives and his friends from the synagogue had arrived. Joanna's aunts and uncles, and grandparents, and all her friends, and all who had known and loved the laughing little girl were there, weeping and crying because she was dead.

Jesus waved His hand at the crowd who had followed Him to stay back. Only Peter and John and James—and Jairus—could go in with Him.

On the doorstep, Jesus spoke to the men and women and children who were weeping for Joanna.

"Why are you making this ado, and weeping?" He asked gently. "The little girl is not dead. She only sleeps!"

And the family and friends stared at the tall Man in the white robe, and laughed at Him through their tears, and yelled at Him, and tried to put Him out. They knew that Joanna was truly dead, and the words of Jesus sounded to them cruel, and strange, because they did not believe in Him.

But Jesus went inside the house, with Peter and James and John and Jairus. He went to Joanna's mother, and wiped her tears. He took her arm and led them all upstairs to the darkened room where the child lay, white and motionless.

Jesus bent over the bed. He lifted up one cold, limp hand, and murmured:

"Little girl, arise!"

And as He spoke, Joanna opened her eyes, and stretched, and got out of bed, and walked straight into her mother's and father's arms.

"She is alive. She was dead and she lives! O Lord, thank You!" said Jairus, as he held her close.

Tears of joy streamed down the mother's cheeks, as she stared open-mouthed at Jesus, and fell to her knees before Him to adore Him.

Jesus, with the most pleased and tender and understanding smile, leaned down to look in Joanna's eyes.

"Give her something to eat," He said gently. Any little girl called back from death to life would probably be hungry.

Jesus straightened up to His full height, and His bearded face grew solemn. One more thing, He said: *Tell no one what has happened here.*

For one last instant Jesus laid His hand on Joanna's black curls, then taking Peter and James and John with Him, He went silently down the stairs, and past the weeping aunts and uncles and friends, and out the door of Jairus' house. And the crowd who had waited for Him, followed Him back to the beach.

Joanna's mother hurried off to fix her some fresh bread and butter, and a cup of bubbly cold milk. Downstairs the relatives and friends who had been weeping were noisy with questions.

"What happened? Is she really alive now? Did Jesus really bring her back from death? Tell us! Tell us!" they gabbled. "You look so happy, something fine must have happened."

But Joanna's mother only smiled and said nothing, as Jesus had commanded. These were the people who had laughed at Him, and who had not believed when He came. Let them wonder now. Let them ask and get no answer. For Jesus had no use for those who could not believe.

And upstairs, holding his daughter close, Jairus whispered:

"My dearest daughter, no matter what happens in your life, always believe."

He held her chin in his hands. "Sometimes," he said, "you will wonder why God lets terrible things happen—why He does not hurry to answer your prayers. And sometimes you will not understand Him at all. But always you must trust Him, and believe, even when His answer to your prayer is No."

Jairus hugged her close.

"Remember, what Jesus said to me. He said 'Fear not. Only *believe*.' "

And Joanna repeated the great secret of Jesus:

"Fear not. Only *believe!* "

And though Jairus and his wife and Joanna obeyed Jesus and never told anyone what happened, the story spread faster than sunrise. The doctors, the relatives, the friends who had seen her die, saw Joanna alive again, laughing and singing, and growing to be a beautiful woman. And they who saw her told everyone they knew about the miracle, and eventually it was written down for us by St. Matthew, and St. Mark and St. Luke so that we could share the secret Joanna had learned from the Lord.

Jesus Comes Home

THE whole town of Nazareth was talking about Jesus. Now that He was so famous everybody liked to boast that Jesus had been his closest friend—even the people who had never bothered to speak to Him before. Grown men remembered wrestling with Jesus long ago when they were boys together in the synagogue school. People bragged about the table or a wagon they had bought that Jesus had made in His carpenter shop. Old men liked to tell of the days when Jesus had been little, and they had given Him an orange or a fig as a treat.

Naturally, Jesus had many relatives in Nazareth, cousins, uncles and aunts, and even more distant relatives, all of them known in the language of the day as His "brethren." Some of His cousins—James and Jude and Simon—had become His apostles. But the others had not paid much attention to Jesus until He became famous for His preaching and His miracles. And then they began to be a little jealous, and to say:

"Wouldn't you think Jesus would be proud of His relatives and want to show us off a bit?"

And "He hasn't paid any attention to us at all!"

So some of His brethren went to see Mary, His mother, in her little white house in Nazareth.

"Mary, we want to go down to Capernaum to see Jesus. He has been away from home for about a year, and He seems to have forgotten all about us. Will you come with us?"

Mary smiled. She knew what they were thinking. She herself did not mind that Jesus seemed to ignore her. She knew He had not forgotten, and she remembered the words He had spoken so many years before:

"Do you not know I must be about My Father's business?"

He was about His Father's business, now, and Mary had no intention of interfering. Still, she would enjoy a chance to see Him again, even from a distance.

With these relatives Mary walked from Nazareth down to the bulging overcrowded town of Capernaum where Jesus was preaching.

In the private house where Jesus was staying, the crush of the crowds was overpowering. Sick and well, everyone wanted to see Jesus, to touch Him and talk to Him. Mary stood far back on the fringe of the crowd, watching. But some of her big-shouldered relatives began to shove their way forward until they got through the door of the house right in the sight of Jesus.

"Look!" they cried out. "Your mother and your brethren are waiting for You outside!"

And they grinned, sure that He would clear a pathway through the crowd and rush out to greet the family from Nazareth.

Jesus, looking over their heads and past the crowd, saw Mary waiting beyond. For a moment their eyes met in loving greeting. He knew that she had walked a long and weary journey to see Him, and He longed to comfort her. And she knew that He must still be about God's business. They smiled in perfect, silent understanding.

With His eyes still smiling His love for Mary, Jesus spoke to the crowd:

"Who is My mother? And My brethren?"

He flung His arms wide to bless them all.

"Look at My mother and My brethren!" He cried.

"Whoever shall do the will of God, He is My brother and My sister and mother."

Mary smiled, because she understood. But His relatives were disgusted, and they hurried away from Jesus with angry frowns.

Back in Nazareth they told everyone that Jesus had become too famous and important to bother speaking to His own mother and family. And no matter how Mary objected and tried to explain, people listened to them and believed them.

Even on street corners people were arguing about Jesus.

"Why does He stay in Capernaum? Why doesn't He come here and preach in His own home town?" complained a shopkeeper with a crooked chin.

"If He came to Nazareth crowds would follow Him here too, and my rooms would be full for a change!" said a red-faced innkeeper.

"Is He ashamed of Nazareth? Or is He afraid that if He comes here people will find out that He's just a plain carpenter? I bet He couldn't work a single miracle here," said a paunchy little fat man who had never liked the clear-eyed Boy Jesus when they had gone to school together.

Then without warning, Jesus suddenly returned to Nazareth. Mary's home was surrounded with people, some laughing and poking fun at the Nazarene Who had become famous, and others shouting friendly greetings. After their meal, Peter and the others had trouble clearing room for Jesus to walk to the synagogue, where He had promised to preach.

Everyone in town was there, waiting to see what this Man Who had been their neighbor would do and say.

Jesus stood before them, in the same synagogue where He had prayed and studied as a child. And because it was the Sabbath day they gave Him the Scriptures to read aloud. And He chose the part of what is called the Old Testament where words of Isaias the prophet are written, and He read to them:

"The Spirit of the Lord is upon Me. He has anointed Me to preach the gospel to the poor. He has sent Me to heal those who are sorry for their sins. And to preach freedom to those who are not free, and sight to the blind, to free those that are bruised. And to preach the acceptable year of the Lord, and the day of reward."

When Jesus had folded up the scroll on which the Scripture was written, He gave it back to the head of the synagogue, and sat down. And the eyes of everyone in that house of worship were watching Him.

And He said to them:

"Today the Scripture you have heard, is fulfilled."

Row after row of His townsfolk in the benches started whispering to each other.

"What does He mean?" they said. "Does He dare to say that He is the Savior the Scriptures tell of?"

"Imagine saying such a thing!" they whispered with raised eyebrows and shocked eyes. "Isn't this the Carpenter? He's just a plain Man from this very town. He's no Savior!"

"If He's all He says He is—why does He sit there just talking? Why doesn't He show us á miracle or two, like He did in Capernaum?"

Jesus knew what they were thinking, and He said:

"Doubtless you will say to Me: . . . As great things as You have done in Capernaum, do here in Your own country also."

And then He reminded them of the stories in their holy books about the prophets of old. He reminded them that when the famous Elias was on earth, God sent him not to the people of Israel who did not really believe in Him, but to a widow in the far-off country of Sidon. The same was true of other holy men. Those close to them who should have believed in them, only laughed—and God sent the prophets to other countries and other people who did believe.

"A prophet is not without honor," said Jesus, "except in his own country."

A grumbling filled the synagogue. He called Himself a prophet, did He? Wasn't He the son of Mary? He had grown up in these very streets and prayed before this very altar, hadn't He? How could He be a prophet or a Savior?

And they began to make shrill noises and mocking faces and stamp their feet. He had not done a single miracle. He had not cured anyone in Nazareth. Yet He pretended to be close to God? Bah!

With loud cries of anger they rushed upon Him, these unbelieving men of Nazareth. They dragged Him out into the narrow street, and up to the edge of the hill on which the town was built. They hated Him, these old neighbors of His. They wanted to destroy Him, as if He were the worst criminal on earth.

"Throw Him over the cliff! Let Him work a miracle then—this Carpenter with a swelled head!"

They dragged Him closer and closer to the edge, high above the jagged rocks.

And then suddenly—Jesus was gone.

No one in the crowd could tell where He had gone or how. A moment He was there, the next instant gone.

And even to this day, those who are closest and nearest to Jesus, and who have every reason to believe Him, are the ones who mock Him, and would destroy Him. But no one can destroy the Son of God.

The Boy with the Five Loaves

JESUS and His disciples had gone away.

For long hours they had preached, and healed the sick, without stopping even to eat. At last they could give no more. With the Master they climbed into Peter's boat and sailed across the Sea of Galilee to a deserted part of the shore, far from any town, hoping to find silence, and rest, and peace for prayer.

But some in the crowd had overheard the apostles' plans, and they told others. The wind had barely begun to fill Peter's sails when the crowd started down the beach on foot, determined to meet Jesus on the other side of the sea. They forgot He needed rest. They knew only that they needed Him, and that He would never turn them away.

They put their sick relatives and friends on litters and stretchers, ready to carry them four times around the sea if only the Master would heal them. They slung their babies on their shoulders. They grabbed handfuls of fruit and nuts to munch along the way. They called to their neighbors and to people on the streets to join them. And singing and laughing they started the long walk to the place where they knew Peter planned to put his boat ashore.

"Drop what you're doing and come," they called. "Come quickly, before it is too late!"

A little boy in a faded brown robe was perched on the edge of the town well when he heard that call. Quicker than a field mouse he darted home, and burst into the kitchen. His mother was pulling sweet-smelling loaves of new-baked bread from the oven.

"Can I go too, Mother? Huh? Can I go?"

Hands on her hips, she looked at him. "Well, Seth, you are a big boy of eleven now. Yes, you may go. But stay close to the others, and don't get lost. And—you must take some food."

"Oh, Mother! No!" Seth protested, but in vain.

"I'll be too late," he said, as his mother wrapped two freshly baked fish in cool green leaves and placed them in a basket.

"No one else is taking food. I'll look like a baby," he wailed. And then: "That's too much to carry, and too much for me to eat!"

His mother wrapped five loaves of new barley bread in clean muslin and packed them in the basket.

"No son of mine will go anywhere without some food, not even to follow the Master, so long as I am here to pre-

pare it. And you will take more than you need, Seth, to have
some to share if the others bring none. That surely is what
the Master would tell you to do."

She kissed him on the forehead. "I have a feeling you
will be glad you waited for this," she said. "Have a good
time! And Seth—don't lose that basket!"

"I won't." Seth turned and ran down the path, through
the streets, and down to the beach, as fast as his sandals
could carry him. But the crowds were already almost out
of sight around the curving shore of the lake. Their laughter and singing echoed over the gentle waves.

"If I hadn't had to wait for this basket," grumbled
Seth, "I'd be with them now. Of all the stupid things, having to carry a lunch!"

He tried singing to himself as he hurried over the sand,
but his voice was thin and his breath came hard, so he
stopped. The basket was heavy, and the handle pressed into
his fingers. He switched it to the other hand.

"It's lonesome walking alone like this," Seth said out
loud. "I could stop, right here. I don't have to go to hear
Jesus. I've heard Him before."

Then he answered himself. "Why should I stop? I
want to go to Jesus. Wherever He is. Don't ask me
why——" he said to a bird wheeling overhead. "I don't
know enough to tell you in words. But I know inside me."

Seth looked around to be sure no one else had overheard him. And he threw back his shoulders and held his
chin high, and strode along the way his father did when they
walked together.

But the basket was heavy, and awkward. It bumped
against his legs. And the sun was higher now, and hot.
Prickles of sweat started on his neck.

"I could hide the basket, and pick it up on the way
home," he said to himself. But suppose some wanderer
found it, and stole it? Seth clenched his lips and walked on.

"I could say I lost it," he thought, kicking at the pebbles. "I could go so fast without it!" For a moment he put it down. Then he picked it up with the other hand. He had promised his mother. And besides, why bother to go to Jesus if you were already planning a lie in your heart?

His hair fell over his eyes, and stuck damply to his cheeks. His feet hurt, and the basket grew heavier every second. He walked on, past the great black boulder, around a shining blue inlet, up over the dunes. He walked and walked. Noon had passed, and the heat rising from the white sand was blinding.

Seth dropped the basket to the ground, and watched it wobble and teeter till it came to rest at a crooked angle against the gray and brown rocks. He straightened his fingers and studied the four whitish blisters that had risen on his palm. His stomach rumbled and gurgled with hunger.

"I could eat some now," he said to the waves, "and the basket would be lighter, and easier to carry."

Then he shook his head in answer. "Mother gave me the food to share. So I should wait till I get there. I'll be hungrier then, anyway. Wonder how far it is now?" Even though no one else could hear him, Seth made his voice sound strong and brave, because listening to it made him feel better!

He squinched his eyes and peered down the beach. Far off he could see where the crowd had stopped—and there by the shore was a swaying black dot that must be Peter's boat.

"They found Him!" said Seth to the wind. "If I hurry I can get there in an hour or so."

Rescuing the basket, he started off again. But he could not keep his eyes on the spot where Jesus was. He must watch where he walked, careful of stones and scrub pine, and vines to trip over. His nose itched. His legs were so tired the calves of them twitched. His sandal straps rubbed at his heels. And suddenly he was lonely, more lonely than in all his eleven years of life, and here where no one could see him, Seth came very close to tears.

He lost track of time. He simply walked. An hour passed. Another. Perspiration and tears stung his eyes and cheeks. Angrily he rubbed his eyes with his fist, and walked. . . .

The sun was low over the Sea when Seth finally saw Jesus. He saw no one else. Without thinking he walked right through the crowds up to the very front row of the giant circle of faces around the Master. With a sigh he sank to his knees on the grass, and laid his hand on the basket lid. Jesus was speaking, and His words flowed over Seth like a cool breeze, smoothing his cheek, caressing his hair. For once Seth did not listen to the words themselves. He heard only the love in Jesus' voice. Eyes closed, Seth listened, and understood with his heart.

The sun sank steadily over the Sea. The sky purpled with twilight. The first star shone in the west. And Jesus' voice fell silent.

Seth opened his eyes. Not twelve feet from him the apostles huddled around the Master, their faces grave. Seth heard Philip say:

"Lord, this is a desert place, and the dinner hour has already passed. Send these people away now, so that they can go to the next villages and towns and buy themselves meat to eat."

Seth's eyes widened, as he heard Jesus reply: "They have no need to go. *Give* them something to eat!"

And Philip gazing out at the crowd said shyly to his Master, "Lord—two hundred pence would not buy enough food for all these!"

Seth scrambled to his feet. Taking his basket, he ran to the nearest apostle, the fisherman named Andrew.

"I have some food," he said. "Not much. But take it!
I'm—I'm not hungry. My mother made me bring this."

Andrew bent down and grasped Seth's shoulders with
a welcoming smile. "Do you realize you're the only person
here with any food at all? My brother, Peter, and the rest
of us went and asked everyone. Not even a fig left in the
whole crowd!"

Andrew peered at Seth's dirt-smeared face. He saw the
streaks of dried sweat, and the tangled hair, and the blisters
on his palm. "You worked hard to carry that food. Who
knows? You may not know what you have done. Come!"

With his hand firmly on Seth's shoulder, Andrew led
him straight to Jesus. "Lord," said the apostle, "there is a
boy here who has five loaves of barley bread, and two fishes."
Andrew paused, then added lamely. "But—what are these
among so many?"

Jesus looked at Seth, and the dark eyes of the Son of
God seemed to brighten the twilight with their smile. Those
eyes seemed to Seth to be looking into the corners of his
heart, and to be pleased, and to say a silent: "Well done!"

Then Jesus said to Andrew and the others: "Make the
men sit down!" For many people, seeing that night had
overtaken them and that Jesus had stopped preaching, were
already preparing to start the long walk home. The apostles
went out among the crowd, urging them to stay, and telling
them to sit on the grass in rows of fifty and a hundred by
families. Then the apostles counted, to see how many must
be fed.

"Lord," said Peter at last, "there are five thousand
men—and their wives and children, too. Five thousand!"

For answer Jesus unwrapped Seth's five loaves of
bread. Standing, He took the bread and raised it toward
heaven, and gave thanks to God, and blessed it. Then He
broke the loaves into pieces, and began giving them to the

apostles to feed the crowd. Then He took the two baked fish from their wrapper of leaves, and gave thanks again, and blessed them, too, and broke them in pieces.

Seth sucked his cheeks in silent wonder.

At first the apostles took the pieces of bread and fish in their hands to give away. But their hands could not hold all the pieces! One by one they scurried off to get baskets, their eyes wide with astonishment.

At the touch of Jesus the bread and fish seemed to multiply, and grow. Piece after piece the Lord broke off, and still the food was not gone. Andrew and Philip and Peter hurried off with full baskets, and the others of the twelve as well, and when they came back Jesus filled them again and again. Row after row of people, hundred after hundreds, ate of those five loaves and two fishes. There were even second helpings for those who needed more!

Andrew had given Seth his share immediately but Seth held it, waiting to see if there would really be enough for everyone. An hour passed, and the five thousand ate their fill, and the apostles, and even Jesus. And in the growing darkness, Seth ate too.

Andrew came and sat beside him on the cool grass. "Do you know what you have done?" whispered Andrew.

"I have seen a miracle," said Seth. "That I know."

"You have helped to make a miracle," Andrew said. "Your mother and you. I do not know what it cost you in trouble and pain and weariness, but He knows. And look what He has made of the little you offered!"

Then the voice of Jesus sounded quietly as He spoke to the apostles: "Gather up the pieces that remain, lest they be lost!"

Seth whispered in Andrew's ear. "Why should He bother with the leftovers, when by a miracle He can feed thousands?"

Andrew smiled. "Even God does not waste His gifts.

Neither should we!" And rising to his feet he went with the others, to gather the pieces. When they were through the fragments of bread filled twelve baskets. More remained than Seth had brought!

From the crowd came a murmur. And the murmur grew to a rumbling, and the rumbling to a roar.

"This is in truth the prophet we have been promised! This Jesus is the Messiah!"

And suddenly, the crowd was moving toward Jesus crying: "Lord, be our King!" "A King!"

Seth craned his neck to see the face of Jesus. The Master stood shaking His head in gentleness, and even sadness, as the crowd approached. Not for a king's crown had He come to the world!

With outstretched arms Jesus tried to stop them, these miracle-filled men who did not yet understand the Kingdom of God. He turned to His apostles, and gave them orders: they were to get into Peter's boat and sail home without Him.

Then, leaving the puzzled crowd behind Him, Jesus turned and hurried up the mountainside alone to pray.

Seth also walked alone that night. There were people all around him, talking as they made the long journey home around the beach. But Seth, his empty basket swinging at his side, hardly heard them. In the light of the torches he saw only the eyes of Jesus as they had looked at him and smiled.

"Why did He not want to be King?" he wondered. "I have heard Him speak of the kingdom of heaven, but I do not know what He means. All I know is that He is *my* King. And I shall love Him, and honor Him, and obey His word till I die."

And hugging the secret of the miracle to his heart, Seth hurried homeward to tell his mother of the wonders that had been done, the wonder God had made from her five loaves of new barley bread, and her two fresh-baked fish.

The One Who Walked on the Waters

AT Jesus's command, the twelve apostles started home
alone.

After the miracle of the loaves and the fishes,
when He had fed the five thousand, His apostles had been too
filled with wonder to speak. But the crowd by the shore, fed
by that miracle, had swarmed over Jesus and begged Him to
be their King. It was then that He had ordered the twelve to

set sail for home without Him. And He had gone alone to the
mountain-top to pray.

The crowds still roared for the Master as the twelve
went quietly down to Peter's boat in the darkness.

"He must be our King!" they cried. "We will make
Him King!"

"A Man who can work miracles like this can make our
country free. He can drive out the Romans and free us! Jesus
the King, save us!"

Silently the apostles waded out through the inky waters
and climbed into the boat. With long practice they took their
places. One hauled up the anchor, three manned the sails.
Others stood ready with the oars. And Peter took charge of
the helm. The staunch old boat creaked companionably as
it slipped obediently off into the night.

As the wind took hold of the sails, Nathanael Bartholomew broke the silence.

"Twelve baskets of food left over! And only five loaves
and two fishes to start with. Who can understand that?"

Thomas, in his deep voice answered: "No one can say
they don't believe it. We saw it. Everyone saw it. Five thousand men—and their wives and children."

"Who can understand what Jesus does?" asked Peter.
"I wish I understood Him! So often I wonder who He
is, really."

"No mere man can do what He does," said his brother,
Andrew. "He is more than a great teacher, more than a
prophet. I do not dare say what I think He is!"

"The people really wanted to make Him a king, and He
refused. That I shall never understand," said the oily voice
of Judas Iscariot. "Isn't it peculiar, not to want to be King?"

Simon, one of Jesus' cousins, snorted at Judas. "I don't
pretend to understand Him—but this I know. He does not
need to be a king on this earth. He is more than that."

"For our sakes, He could have become King!" said

Judas Iscariot stubbornly. "We have followed Him, without a penny of reward. If He were King we could be pretty important people. Why should He refuse?"

No one answered. Secretly they were all glad that the darkness kept them from even looking Judas in the face, so shocked were they by what he had said. Of all of them Judas seemed the furthest from understanding the Master. They felt uneasy with him, without knowing why.

The night was black, blacker than usual, they realized in the silence. No stars hung in the sky. And while they had been talking a wind had risen. No idle breeze this, but a gale! The ship was making little headway now, and the timbers groaned as she battled the storm. So dark was it that they could see only the angry white crests of the waves swelling around them. Spray dashed over the boat, and spindrift clung to their beards.

"Ai! Ai!" Judas cried. "We shall die in such a storm. So suddenly it came! The work of devils or evil spirits it must be. And no one can save us!"

And John, shouting over the wind, answered, "Have you forgotten the tempest we were in before, when Jesus was sleeping in the boat? And how He awoke and ordered the wind and the sea to be still? That was no worse than this!"

"I wish He were here now," said James. "Without Him we are helpless!"

The wind blew harder, and the waves rose higher. The boat rocked till the mast itself nearly touched the water, and even Peter, the best sailor of them all, clung to the sides in alarm.

The boat righted itself again, and Peter raised his hand to his eyes, peering through the storm.

"Look!" he cried hoarsely, his voice choked with fear.

The others followed his pointing arm, and gasped.

They saw the figure of Jesus, calm and serene, walking across the waves!

"It is a ghost," said Philip, his face white.

"That can't really be Jesus," said Simon.

"We're all seeing things that aren't there," said Jude Thaddeus, his brother, and his voice shook with fear.

Terror gripped them all, and grown men though they were, they cried out in fear till their voices were louder than wind or sea.

Across the waves came the voice of Jesus:

"Be of good heart! It is I—have no fear!"

The apostles, gripping the sides of the boat with tight-clenched fists, stared at each other wild-eyed, wondering if the darkness and the tempest could have made them all mad. And yet, knowing Jesus, they dared not dismiss what they saw.

Peter alone found his voice. "Lord!" he called, "If it is really You, tell me to come to You and walk on the waters too!"

Over the crash of the waves and the roar of the gale all twelve heard the answer plain:

"Come!" said Jesus, in that strong and loving voice they knew so well!

Peter looked at the others, and even in the storm they could see him smile with faith. Wrapping his long robe around his waist, Peter crawled over the side of the boat. For an instant his feet hung over the sea. Then he pushed himself off—and landed on top of the waves as firmly as if they were solid ground!

Head high, arms outstretched, Peter walked over the waters to Jesus.

But the wind was strong, and the storm still raged. White foam from the waves splattered on Peter's chest, and on his long wind-tossed beard. He took his eyes from Jesus, and looked at the waters, and he grew afraid. It is impossible! he thought to himself. I can't really be walking on the water. I shall drown, I know!

And the moment Peter grew afraid, he began to sink. The waves lost their firmness, and the water swallowed him up. Down he went into the black sea, and the waves closed over him. Struggling and battling he brought his head above water, thrashing wildly against the storm.

"Lord!" he screamed. "Save me!"

And immediately Jesus was beside him. He stretched out His hand to Peter, and took hold of him, and pulled him up till Peter stood beside Him on top of the water.

"Oh you of little faith," said Jesus, "why did you doubt?"

And Jesus led Peter back across the sea, and into the boat. And the moment Jesus reached the boat, the wind stopped.

The apostles fell to their knees as Jesus stepped into the boat.

"Indeed," they said. "You are the Son of God."

Peter, his robes cold and soaking wet, his hair bedraggled from the storm, knelt before Jesus.

"The Son of God!" he whispered. "The Son of God."

But Jesus only smiled, and told them to sail through the calmed waters, back to Capernaum as they had planned. They had called Him the Son of God, but He knew they had not yet learned all that that name meant. Much more would they have to know before they realized Who Jesus really was. And many times more they would lose faith in Him and doubt, as Peter had done when he fell into the sea.

Jesus, sitting in the peaceful boat, His eyes fixed on the dark skies, seemed to be thinking, as He had said so long before:

"Greater things than this you shall see!"

Mystery on the Mountain

"Y̶OU know," said Peter, "I am beginning to think that each miracle Jesus works is to teach us a special lesson—like a story to prove His point."

Philip nodded. "But He does not always tell us the lesson immediately. I have been wondering about the loaves and fishes. What could that mean?"

Simon, the Lord's cousin, shook his head. "Many people do not believe that ever happened. They say it's a fairy tale, because they were not there to see it—or eat of it!"

"I can understand them," grinned Thomas. "I wouldn't have believed it, either—if I weren't there. But what could it mean?"

Jesus, the teacher, Jesus, the Son of God, knew what they were thinking, and He knew that many did not believe the miracle of the loaves and fishes. And, so that no one should ever doubt, so that everyone then and now would listen to the meaning of that miracle, Jesus did it again.

As always, crowds followed Him wherever He went, some out of love, and some out of plain curiosity. The time of this second miracle, Jesus led the throngs far from home, walking with them into the wilderness for three days! Without a murmur they followed Him, but as the days passed the food they had brought with them did not last, and they grew hungry.

As before, Jesus sent His apostles scouting among the

159

audience to collect all the food they had left—and this time there were seven loaves of bread, and a few little fishes among four thousand people. No doubt of that, either.

In front of their eyes Jesus gave thanks, and blessed the food, and multiplied it, so that all were fed. And everyone counted the baskets of leftovers carefully gathered. Seven baskets!

And standing before them, Jesus reminded them that it is recorded in the Scriptures that many centuries before, God had given the Jews in the desert manna to eat, food from heaven. And Jesus said:

"My Father gives you the true bread from heaven. For the bread of God is that which comes down from heaven, and gives life to the world."

With one voice the people answered: "Lord—give us always of this bread!"

Then Jesus answered with a message so strange that no one moved lest they should miss a word of what He was saying:

"I am the bread of life!" He said, in a voice clearer and sharper than thunder. "He who comes to Me shall not hunger, and He that believes in Me shall not thirst."

And as He spoke even the wind in the trees was still.

"I came down from heaven," said Jesus slowly. "I came down from heaven not to do My own will, but the will of Him that sent Me."

And: "Now this is the will of the Father who sent Me: that everyone who sees the Son, and believes in Him, may have life everlasting!"

The people looked at each other in amazement. They did not like the sound of that! The same people who had been so delighted to see Him work wonders, so proud to eat of the miraculous loaves and fishes, now began to grumble and growl.

"Who does He think He is, anyway?" they said.

"Isn't this Jesus of Nazareth? Just a plain carpenter, the son of Mary? What right has He to say He came down from heaven?"

And others said: "What does He mean calling Himself 'the bread of life?' "

With the crumbs of bread still clinging to their beards they got to their feet, and turned their backs on Jesus, and walked away. They were willing to believe He was a great wonderworker, and a fine Teacher, and a very good Man. But they refused to believe that He had come from heaven.

"If He came from heaven, why isn't He dressed in a crown, and a golden robe?" they snorted. "If God is His Father, why does He walk the roads like an ordinary Man?"

They left Him, because He was what God wanted Him to be—and that was not what they wanted Him to be! Shocked and angry, they left, hundreds and thousands of men and women who had followed Him for years.

Finally Jesus called the twelve apostles to Him. Gravely He studied their faces.

"Will you also go away?" He asked.

Peter answered for them. In the fisherman's face Jesus could see that he did not yet understand all that the Master had said or meant. No man can understand until God shows him! But Peter said: "Lord—to whom shall we go? You have the words of eternal life."

That was enough. Jesus smiled. Peter, He knew, already believed. And God would help him to understand.

Then Jesus led them down by the springs of the River Jordan, and sat with them watching the water pour out of the mountainside down to the stream.

"Whom do people say that I am?" Jesus asked.

John and James, Andrew and shy Philip answered Him, telling Jesus the strange ideas that people had of Him. Of those who still followed Him and had not turned away, some thought Jesus was actually John the Baptist come back to life, with his head magically back on his shoulders! And others thought He might be Elias, the famous prophet who had lived hundreds of years ago, returned to earth by some miracle.

Philip smiled. "We know You are not either of those."

"But whom do *you* say that I am?" Jesus asked.

There was a moment's silence. Then Peter stirred, and his eyes shone, and he looked around first at the water, and then at the blue sky, and then at Jesus. Then Peter stood up, and his voice was strangely quiet:

"You are the Christ! The Son of the living God!"

And Jesus answered: "Blessed are you! Because flesh and blood has not revealed this to you, but My Father, who is in heaven. And I say to you: You are Peter, and upon this rock I will build My church, and the gates of hell shall not prevail against it. And I will give you the keys of the kingdom of heaven!"

Then, at once, Jesus turned to the twelve apostles with a new command. Tell no one else, He said, that I am the Christ, the Son of God. The time will come when the world will know. Till then, keep it secret.

And as they stared at Him, puzzlement in their eyes, Jesus began to explain the things that lay in the future for Him, and for them. It was not what they expected to hear. Their faces grew thin with horror as they listened.

The day will come, said Jesus, when I must go to Jerusalem. And the agents of the chief priests of the Temple, and the scribes and the Pharisees will have Me arrested. And I will suffer many things, and be put to death! And on the third day I will rise again.

Peter groaned aloud: "Lord! No! These things shall not happen to You!"

With fire in His eyes Jesus turned to Peter:

"Go behind Me, Satan!" He said to the man He had just called blessed. "You are a scandal to Me, because you do not

understand the things that are of God, but only the things that are of men!"

Poor Peter! He still did not understand. It is not an easy thing to believe that the Man who is the Son of God should have to suffer and die. Yet that was in God's plan, the supreme mystery of all the ages.

And men, apostles of yesterday or Christians of today, can understand the mysteries of God only when God Himself helps them, and opens the eyes of their mind so they can see. The day would come, in God's good time, when Peter and the others would understand. Till then, they must be patient to follow Him as children follow, trusting and believing, always. Step by step He would lead them—and the next step was near at hand.

Only six days later Jesus called Peter and James and John to follow Him on a special journey, an adventure that would bring them closer to heaven than any man had yet been. Only those three out of the twelve were called, and they did not know why, or where they were going.

Through the Valley of Esdraelon He led them, up the windswept slopes of Mount Tabor, almost to the top, near a rippling, whispering stream. Without a word Jesus knelt on the stubble and dried-up grass to pray. The others knelt beside Him. The only sound was the splash of water in the stream, and the stirring of the wind. . . .

Suddenly the three apostles realized that something extraordinary was happening! Something they could not explain, some surge of new power, had come over their Master. He was not now as He had been even five minutes before.

The shape of His face had changed! And, a moment later, they saw with their own eyes how His clothes changed —and became white and glittering.

The robe that Jesus wore was the robe of a teacher of

Palestine, long and flowing, and no matter how clean in the morning, it was always stained by dust before He had walked far. But now the robe was pure and shining, as if woven not of cotton and wool, but of a stuff softer and more radiant than anything on this earth. Whiter than snow the robe was now, whiter than a cloud beside the sun.

"He is being transfigured before us," Peter whispered.

Suddenly from the heavens came two other figures, men who shone like stars, and they began talking with Jesus! One was Moses, the great leader of the Jews, into whose hands God had given the Ten Commandments, hundreds and hundreds of years before. The other was Elias, the famous prophet of the Old Testament, who had gone up to heaven in a fiery chariot, centuries and centuries ago.

The three fishermen, Peter, James, and John, knelt on the mountain-top, and saw Jesus with Moses and Elias, and heard them talk, the living with the dead. And it was too much for the apostles, this meeting of heaven and earth! They were overcome, their minds grew slow, their eyelids heavy, and they fell asleep. . . .

They never knew how long they slept. Only that as they awoke, rubbing their eyes, light was shining around their beloved Jesus. The two visitors from heaven, Moses and Elias, were vanishing, walking off as it were into another world.

"Master!" said Peter eagerly. "It is good for us to be here. Let us make three altars. One for You. One for Moses. One for Elias." And Peter grinned, not understanding that what he had said was ridiculous, for the only altar that could ever be built was for Jesus and the Father.

Instantly a bright cloud appeared overhead, and blotted out the sun. And they heard a Voice saying: "This is My beloved Son in Whom I am well pleased. Hear Him!"

The three apostles heard that voice of God, and fell on their faces in fear. Then Jesus bent over and touched them, and said, "Arise, and do not be afraid."

No more voices then. No more shining figures. Only Jesus smiling, and the clear breeze blowing over the sunlit summit of Mount Tabor.

And as they went down the mountain, Jesus said:

"Tell no man what you have seen, till the Son of Man shall be risen from the dead."

The mystery was closer than ever, the mighty mystery of Jesus, who was Son of God, and Son of Man, and yet Who must suffer and die, and *Who would one day rise from the dead.*

That was the one overpowering phrase, the idea that was still beyond them. *Rise from the dead?*

Peter and James and John had seen Him shining in the glory of Godhood, transfigured, more radiant than the sun. They had seen Him speak with men long dead, with Moses and Elias. They knew He had every power of heaven at His command. Had they not seen Him feed the thousands, and walk on the waves? Had not they stood in the bedroom of Jairus' daughter and seen Him raise her from the dead? Surely He was, as He said, the Son of God, and with God all things are possible.

Yet now He walked beside them, tall and straight in His dusty robe, truly a Man. Gone was the radiance, the crowning light, and beside them strode Jesus of Nazareth, their teacher, their Master—and their friend.

He was a Man. And He was God. That by itself was almost too much to understand.

Gladly they kept silence about the vision on Mount Tabor. But though they did not speak of it, the glory of that afternoon glowed like the fire of faith in their hearts.

The Fish

THE spies from the Temple were always at the heels of Jesus.

The more the chief priests in Jerusalem heard about Jesus of Nazareth, the more alarmed they became. Every miracle that He performed they heard about, and in their council chambers they waggled their silver-gray beards and worried.

Sadly, those men of the Temple were not very holy men at all. The people, the thousands of good Jews who prayed in the Temple, were truly religious and loved the Lord their God. But these particular chief priests were more interested in power and in riches than in God, though they took good care not to let the people suspect it.

When they heard about Jesus they did not even stop to think that He might be God. All they knew was that the people of Palestine loved Him and followed Him—and that Jesus was becoming a powerful and dangerous leader.

"If only we could catch Him saying something wrong, or doing something against the law, then we could tell the people and they would follow Him no longer," said the chief priests.

So week after week they sent their spies and agents to

167

follow Jesus, and watch everything He did or said, and if they could, to trap Him into doing something wrong.

One day while the Master was staying in Peter's house in Capernaum, the tax collector came to town—and then the spies thought surely they would trap Jesus!

Taxes have forever been a problem to all kinds of men, and in Palestine two thousand years ago they were a torment and a torture for everyone. The Roman Empire had conquered Palestine, and the Romans were very clever at taking money out of the pockets of people they conquered. There was no end to Roman taxes!

If you lived in Palestine in those days, you paid two taxes on your land, your farms and houses and building lots. If you were a farmer you had to give one tenth of your wheat and one fifth of your wine and fruit to the Romans. You paid a toll to ride the highways, and a tax on everything you bought, even a tax on your own head for the privilege of living and breathing.

Now everyone must pay taxes to his own government, to support the country and meet the bills, yesterday in Palestine or today in our own land. But to pay money to a foreign conqueror, to the cruel Romans who had taken the country away from the Jews of Palestine, was truly painful. After all, the money went off to Rome for the Emperor to spend as he pleased; it was not used to make life better for the people who paid it!

The people of Palestine were growing poorer and poorer. Nearly all their money went in taxes now. Men who had once owned fine big farms had to sell their land to pay the Romans, and many a once rich man was now a beggar in the streets.

When the Roman tax collector came to Capernaum to collect what was called the didrachma, the Temple spies went to see Peter.

"Well, Peter—will your Master pay the tax?"

It was a very clever question. If Jesus said He would pay the tax, the good Jews who followed Him as their leader would resent it. Many of them, like Peter, wondered if it were not even a sin to pay taxes to Rome and Caesar, instead of to Israel, as the law in the Bible said. Yet if Jesus refused to pay the tax, the Romans would arrest Him, and throw Him in a dungeon.

"Will Jesus pay the tax?" asked the spies.

"You'll see," answered Peter with a scowl, and strode into the house.

Peter went straight to the little box where he kept the money he had earned by fishing. Peter knew he had not enough to pay the tax for himself, let alone for the Master. He had not fished nor earned a single coin in nearly two years, ever since he had started to follow Jesus. Still, Peter looked, to see what he could do.

From a corner of the room Jesus spoke:

"What is your opinion?" He asked Peter. "From whom do the kings of the earth receive tribute and taxes? From their own children, or from strangers?"

"From strangers!" said Peter bitterly.

"Then the children are free!" exclaimed Jesus.

Peter cocked his head, and looked at the Master. Did He mean they did not have to pay the tax to Rome?

Jesus smiled. "But that we should not shock and scandalize them, Peter, go to the sea and cast in a fishline and hook. And take the first fish that shall come up. And when you have opened its mouth, you shall find a stater!"

Peter blinked. A stater was a coin worth twice as much as the tax, exactly enough for himself and for the Master. But to find a piece of money in the mouth of a fish?

"You shall find a stater," said Jesus. "Give it to them for Me and you."

Peter had learned not to question what Jesus said. He walked out of the house and past the spies, and the tax collectors, and down to the shore. He dropped his line in the water. Instantly a fish rose to the bait. Expertly Peter hauled it in, beached it, and opened its mouth. Right inside, tucked in its cheek, lay the coin, shining and golden.

With the fish under his arm, to be saved for dinner, Peter walked back to the house. The tax collector, flanked by Roman soldiers, and the grinning agents of the Temple waited outside.

"Well, Peter?" they said. "We saw you go fishing. Do you hope to pay the tax with that scaly creature? Come, come, pay up—in coin!"

Slowly Peter rubbed the stater dry on his sleeve, and blew on it, and watched it sparkle. Then, without a word he dropped it into the tax collector's bag, and went into the house. And there was nothing for the Romans and the Temple spies to do, but scratch their heads—and feel as foolish as they looked!

Later, alone in the kitchen, Peter cleaned the fish, and a haze of wonderment clouded his blue eyes.

What could it mean—to find tax money in a fish's mouth?—he asked himself as he scraped away the silvery scales. And as he worked, Peter found the answer in his thoughts, an answer as true today as it was then.

Whatever you need, thought Peter, God will supply,—if you trust Him, and obey Him—and work.

Money for taxes, or food, or clothes, money for medicine, money for whatever you really need is ready to your hand. Had not Jesus said, in the Sermon on the Mount, that we should not worry about the things we need, because God will take care of us?

What are we to do, thought Peter. Stop worrying, stop scowling, and work. If you are a fisherman, *fish!* Do what you are meant to, and God will provide. The Father knows what His children need!

    As Peter blew on the coals of the kitchen fire to cook his catch, he grinned. If only men would remember that, how much happier they would be.

    "Some day," he thought, "I will tell the world the story of the fish with the gold coin in its mouth!"

    And, of course, he did.

"Little Children!"

"THE kingdom of heaven!" said John slowly. He lay under the gold and gray shadows of the fig tree, his eyes closed in a day dream.

Around him the others of the twelve apostles sat, some leaning against the trunk, some tailor-fashion, some with their bearded chins in their hands. This day they were to take to the road again, walking back to Jerusalem with the Master. They were only waiting for Jesus Himself to be ready. Till then, they sat in Peter's front yard, grateful for a moment's idleness.

"I wonder what His kingdom will be like," said John. "Will there be crowns? And thrones?"

"Don't you remember?" asked Nathanael Bartholomew. "He told us His kingdom was not of this world."

"He doesn't want to be a king," said Judas Iscariot bitterly. "He ran away the time the crowd tried to make Him one."

"Well, whatever it's like," said John smugly, "I guess I'll have an important place in it."

"I suppose you think you'll be sitting at the Lord's right hand," said his brother, James, chewing on a blade of grass.

"Could well be," said John, opening his eyes.

James sat up. "If anybody will, I will!"

Jude Thaddeus laughed. "I guess since the other James and Simon and I are His own cousins, we should come before you!"

172

And in no time at all, Peter's front yard was as full of squabbling and bickering as a hen house. Grown men these were, and the closest followers of Jesus, yet they argued and grew red in the face, and snapped at each other, each insisting he would be the most important one in the kingdom of God.

Finally Peter stood up and raised his hand for silence. "Look here!" he said. "None of us knows what Jesus means by His kingdom. How can we know where we will stand in it? At the right time, we will ask Him."

When the Master came out of the house they followed Him in silence as He led the way out of the gate and into the street.

"Master——" began John, but he did not finish. From every doorway men and women of Capernaum came running to see Jesus, to wave to Him, to call to Him, and bid Him a good journey.

"Lord——" began James, but he too was interrupted. People swarmed around the Master, asking His blessing, and shouting farewells.

Slowly, smilingly, Jesus made His way through the throngs. At one street corner the crowd thinned for an instant, and the disciples could keep silent no longer. Tugging at His sleeve they asked:

"Master! Who do You think will be the greatest in the kingdom of heaven? Which one of us?"

Jesus stopped and looked at His apostles, and sadness darkened His eyes. He seemed to say: Do you still not understand?

Then bending down He singled out one child from the crowd, a little fellow of six years, with twinkling brown eyes and thick unruly hair.

"Come to Me!" He said, and held out His arms. The boy ran to Him, and Jesus cleared a space for Him in the crowd, and held him where all could see.

"In truth I say to you—unless you become as little children, you shall not enter into the kingdom of heaven!" said Jesus.

"And he that receives one such a little child in My name," Jesus continued, "receives Me. But he that shall scandalize one of these little ones that believe in Me, it were better for him that a millstone should be hung around his neck and that he should be drowned in the depths of the sea!"

The apostles looked at each other with dismay. Children were wonderful, that is true!, they thought to themselves. But to become like a little child? It sounded ridiculous. They were grown men, proud of their wisdom and their knowledge. And this chubby-cheeked boy—what could he know that they did not?

Jesus read their thoughts, and a warning flashed in His eyes.

"See that you despise not one of these little ones! For I say to you that their angels in heaven always see the face of My Father, who is in heaven."

Then Jesus rose, His hand still caressing the boy's shock of unruly hair. Sadly but firmly He answered His apostles' question.

"If any man desires to be first—he shall be the last of all!"

The mothers and fathers of Capernaum had listened spellbound to His words. True, they had always seen that the Master enjoyed children. They had seen Him swing them up to His shoulder, seen Him whittle whistles and doll beds for them, watched Him as He gathered them round Him at twilight to hear His stories of the secret ways of God.

But He loved them! Hear what He said—that you must become like a child to enter His kingdom. No man in history, plain teacher or prophet, ever spoke so wondrously about children, save Jesus!

And mothers and fathers pressed toward Him now, bringing their children to Him. Girls and boys they came, ragamuffins and those dressed in finest woolens, fat ones, thin ones, the runny-nosed and the pimple-faced too, freckled and wart-covered, toddlers and babies in their mothers' arms, plain ones and pretty ones, tall and gangly or runt-sized. Jesus welcomed them all.

"Hold on, there!" cried the disciples. "Stand back! This is no way to treat the Master! He is in a hurry, and He has no time——"

But Jesus said: "Let the little children come to Me, and forbid them not! For the kingdom of heaven is for such as these."

And tenderly He laid His hands on the head of each and every child there, and prayed, and blessed them all. And not until He had blessed them all separately, did He stride off down the highway, on His way at last.

The apostles followed in silence, shame-faced, their eyes fixed on the ground.

In their minds the words of Jesus echoed over and over again.

"Unless you become as little children, you shall not enter the kingdom of heaven!"

What did it mean, to become as little children? To be humble, thought John, and gentle. To love God with a whole heart, and no thought of reward, thought James. To trust Him as a Father, and obey Him as a Father, with happiness, and joy, and no questions asked, said Peter to himself. To feel at home with God, and know that He loves you!

"I wish that I were that tousle-haired boy that Jesus held in His arms," said James to his brother John in a whisper.

"I hope with God's help to be like him," answered John. "The secret of heaven is in the hearts of children, in their eyes and in the smile on their lips. Oh that God will give me the heart of a child again!"

The Blind Man

AUTUMN spread a golden carpet over the land, and the leaves turned red, and the harvest time had come. It was the day of the glorious Feast of the Tabernacles, a holy day and a holiday for all who lived in Israel.

Jesus and His apostles had gone to Jerusalem to celebrate the feast, and the air was filled with the sound of trumpets and dulcimers and drums, and the light of festival torches made the night like day.

But for Jesus this was a time of danger, and of trouble. All Jerusalem was talking of Him. In the streets people wondered who He was:

"Is He the Christ?" they asked. "Or is He a prophet? Or is He a charlatan, a faker? Is He a good man, or an evil one? *Who is this Jesus?*"

And in the Temple council chambers, the high priests and the Pharisees who hated Jesus, and feared Him because He had power they had not, plotted against Him.

"The people love Him too much!" they said. "We tell the people not to believe in Him, not to listen to Him, and they pay no attention to us!"

"We must get rid of Him!" said the oily-faced Pharisees. "And there is only one way to do that—kill Him!"

Caiphas, the high priest with the perfumed beard, shook his head firmly. "You cannot kill Him because the people do love Him, and they would be angry and turn against us.

177

No—what we must do is trap Him, and make a fool of Him, and prove that He is no Messiah!"

"It's those miracles that make the crowds love Him," sniffed one of the Pharisees. "Or what they call miracles. Of course they must be fakes. No man can cure the deaf and the dumb and the crippled. No man can make a dead person live again! But Jesus pretends to do this. Now if we could only catch Him at one of these so-called miracles, and show people how He tricks them . . ."

"Ah!" said Caiphas. "We will wait for the next miracle!"

They did not have long to wait. Jesus knew their schemes, and He met them boldly.

For the days of the Feast Jesus had gone regularly into the Temple to teach, right under the angry noses of the Pharisees and the chief priests. And things which He taught in the Temple only made the people of Jerusalem talk about Jesus even more. And some believed Him when He said He was the Son of God. And others, who did not believe Him, grew angry, and muttered against Him, and even picked up stones to throw at Him. But they could not hurt Him.

And everywhere men spoke of Jesus and wondered:

"Is He the Son of God? Or are the chief priests and Pharisees right when they tell us He is a dangerous Man, who breaks the laws, and offends God?"

Only a few days later, on the Sabbath day, Jesus answered that old question again, with a new miracle.

His disciples at His side, Jesus came out of the Temple, and down to the street. There on the ground sat a beggar, a man who had been born blind, and who never in his life had seen the light of the sun. For years he had sat by the Temple, with a clay cup in which kind passersby dropped coins. Everyone knew him.

This day the disciples seeing him, wondered, as so many people still wonder, why God, who is so good, would let anyone be born blind. Was God punishing this beggar? What had he done wrong?

And they asked Jesus: "Master—is it because he sinned, or because his parents sinned, that he was born blind?"

Jesus shook His head. "Neither has this man sinned, nor his parents. He is blind, in order that the works of God may be shown through him."

The disciples scratched their heads. What could that mean?

Jesus looked at the beggar who had never seen the sun, and He said: "I am the light of the world."

Bending down, Jesus spat on the dusty ground, and then with His hands He kneaded the dampened dust into a kind of clay, and spread the clay on the blind man's eyes. And Jesus whispered: "Go—wash in the pool of Siloam."

Without a question, the blind man rose, and taking his cane he felt his way up the steps and on toward the pool. But Jesus led His disciples away, off through the streets.

What a hullabaloo there was then by the Temple courts! The blind man had done as he was told, and when he had washed the clay from his eyes, he screamed:

"I can see!"

And he whirled from side to side, looking and seeing —seeing the blue sky, the white clouds, the sun, the walls of the Temple, the smile on children's faces, the whole wonderful world.

Around him people jabbered: "Isn't this the beggar that was born blind?"

And others said: "It looks like the same man!"

The beggar grinned. "I am he! The same one!" he shouted.

They clamored around him: "Who made you see? Who opened your eyes?"

And he answered: "That Man called Jesus!"

From inside the council chambers, the Pharisees and the chief priests heard the racket, and sent to see what weird story the beggar was telling.

He stood before them and told them exactly what Jesus had done. "And now," he said, "I can see!"

"This is a terrible thing!" said the Pharisees. "This is the Sabbath day, and our law says no man may work on this day. Jesus cured you on the Sabbath? Then He broke the law! Terrible!"

The beggar shrugged. How could it be so terrible?

"What do you have to say about this Man who made you see?" asked one shiny-cheeked Pharisee.

"He has done no wrong," said the beggar. "I think He is a prophet."

"A prophet? Ha!" snorted the Pharisees. And they turned and whispered together:

"You see how dangerous it is to let Jesus make these so-called miracles?"

And one said: "Perhaps it is no miracle at all. Perhaps the man was never really blind. Or maybe he was taking medicine. Let us be sure."

So they sent the Temple guards to fetch the beggar's mother and father, and when the old couple had come, the Pharisees sneered at them and said:

"Is this the son you said was born blind? If he was really blind, how is it that he can see now?"

The old man and the old woman blinked, and smiled.

"Certainly, he is our son. And it is true that he was born blind and never to this day could he see. But who cured him, we don't know. We didn't even know he was cured! Isn't it wonderful?"

And the father said: "Ask him. He is old enough to speak for himself!"

Then the Pharisees looked at each other, wondering what more they could do. And they beckoned the beggar to them, and with sly and oily voices they said,

"Maybe you were a little bit blind. And you can see now. But give thanks to God—not to this Jesus! He could never have cured you. For we know, and we are telling you, that this Man called Jesus is a sinner!"

The beggar looked at them with bright new eyes. "If He be a sinner, I don't know. But one thing I know—once I was blind, and now I can see!"

The Pharisees' faces blackened with anger, and they clenched their fists.

"Stubborn fool!" they screamed.

"Throw that man out!" they ordered the guards.

And a minute later the beggar found himself on the street, bruised and bleeding from his fall.

Now, when Jesus heard that the Pharisees had thrown the beggar out, He took His disciples and went into the streets. Down every alley He marched, and into every back lane searching for him. And not only His disciples followed Jesus then. Some of the Pharisees came too, for they wanted to see what Jesus would do.

At last Jesus found the beggar sitting before the door of his family's house. There were bloodstains on his clothes, and his arms and face were swollen and bruised, but he was smiling. For the first time in his life he was watching the way ants scurry back and forth to their hills—a wonderful thing to see after a life of blindness.

Jesus stopped before him and laid His hand on the man's shoulder, and asked: "Do you believe in the Son of God?"

The beggar stood up, drawn to his feet by the gaze of

the Master. His answer came in a whisper: "Who is He, Lord, that I may believe in Him?"

And Jesus said: "You have seen Him. It is He who talks with you—now!"

The beggar knew the sound of that voice, knew that this was Jesus, the light of the world, Who had made him see. And he sank to his knees at the Lord's feet and said: "I believe, Lord. I believe!"

Then Jesus turned and faced the cruel-eyed Pharisees, and in the sternest tone He said:

"For judgment I am come into this world, that they who do not see may see—and that they who see, may become blind!"

The Pharisees raised their eyebrows, and smirked. And laughingly they said to Him, "Are we also blind?"

And Jesus said: "If you were truly blind, you would not be guilty of sin. But now you say: We see. And so—you are guilty."

But the Pharisees did not understand what He meant. They did not know that Jesus meant that there were two kinds of blindness—one in the eyes, and the other in the soul. A man may have perfect eyesight, and still not see the truth.

Just so it was with the Pharisees. They looked at Jesus, but they saw only a Man from Nazareth. They did not see that He was God. They called themselves wise, and said they knew all things. They said they could see. But they were blind of soul, and they turned away from Him, laughing and sneering, and muttering against Him.

But the beggar who had been blind of eye, looked on Jesus with his eyes and with his soul, and saw the truth.

"Lord! I believe!"

Mary and Martha

THREE friends Jesus had, aside from His disciples, whom He loved very dearly. There was Martha, and her sister Mary, and their brother Lazarus, who lived in the town called Bethany.

For a long time the four had been good friends. At the very beginning of His public teachings, Jesus had met the gentle, shy Lazarus, and Lazarus had brought Him home for supper one night and introduced Him to his sisters. Bethany was only a few miles from Jerusalem, and from then on, whenever He came near the town, Jesus made it His habit to stay with these friends and visit them. Often He had come to preach in the Bethany synagogue, where Lazarus and Martha and Mary worshipped. In fact, it was in that synagogue that Jesus had told the famous story of the Good Samaritan.

It would be hard to find three people more different than these. Lazarus was a hard-working man, but a quiet one, the kind who listens but seldom speaks, who does his good deeds in secret, and never complains of what others do to him. He liked to garden in his spare time, and to make flowers bloom, and he knew how best to prune trees and train vines. He liked the feel and the smell of growing things.

Mary was a thoughtful and dreaming girl, with a mind that was hungry to learn. People in Bethany used to scold Mary and worry about her because she was not forever worrying about her hair and her skin, or primping like other young ladies. She was neat and clean, they admitted, and pretty in her own way, but why was she forever worrying her head about things that didn't concern her? Better that she would learn to sew a fine seam, or to bake a rich cake, and busy herself at home, instead of mooning over thoughts that were too big for her! And Mary, when she heard them speak, only bent her head and smiled.

Now Martha was just the opposite. Martha was the busiest housewife in Bethany—and the most respected. She scrubbed and swept and dusted and washed and ironed and baked and roasted and basted and tasted and spent her days and most of her nights performing all the duties a woman was expected to perform.

Three people, so different, yet Jesus loved them all, equally, which is of course one of the happiest secrets about the Lord.

One day Jesus came to stop at their home. In the cool shadows of the afternoon He sat in the dooryard, talking with Mary, the thinker and dreamer, who sat listening. And they were talking not of things of this world, but of heaven, and of the ways of the kingdom of God. Mary, her black eyes eagerly on the Master's face, asked many questions. She ached to learn every bit she could about the Way and the Truth of Christian life.

But while they talked, from inside the house came a growing clatter of plates and pots and jugs. It was, somehow, a very noisy kitchen this day—almost as if Martha were deliberately making a racket.

Still Jesus and Mary sat talking.

Suddenly Martha, red-faced, hands dripping wet, breath panting, stomped angrily to the doorway. With that terrible politeness that some people use when they are very cross indeed, she spoke to Mary:

"My!" said Martha. "Isn't it nice and cool out here in the yard. I can feel the coolness now that I'm out of the hot kitchen. You know, Mary, we have a great and wonderful Guest tonight, and we must get supper ready. Here you sit, doing nothing, while I bake and stew over a hot fire! Don't think I wouldn't enjoy sitting out here to chat, but after all —someone must make the meal!"

Mary hung her head, and bit her lip. But before she could reply, Martha turned to Jesus,

"Lord, don't You even care that my sister has left me alone to serve? Speak to her, and tell her to help me!"

Mary hopped to her feet, and a blush crept over her cheeks. But Jesus held out His hand to stop her from going in.

"Martha, Martha," He said gently. "You are careful, and troubled about many things. But one thing is necessary. Mary has chosen the best part, which shall not be taken away from her."

Martha opened her mouth wide, and shut it again with a pop.

Never in her born days had she expected such an answer from the Master!

With a swish of her apron, and a toss of her head, she hurried back to the kitchen, as puzzled and unhappy a woman as ever lived.

"What on earth do you suppose He meant?" she said to herself as she pounded the salt into the stew meat.

"He always said He approved of hard work. Am I to blame for doing my job, for goodness' sake? That Mary is just being plain shiftless and lazy sitting out there talking. You'd think she was a man, not a woman with woman's work to do!"

With a sharp blade Martha sliced the onions, a piece of bread between her teeth to keep the tears away.

"Whoever heard of a girl's using her mind instead of her hands?" Martha asked herself.

There—there was the real question!

For in those days the life of girls and of women was far different than what it is today. Only boys learned to read. Only boys went to school. A girl was meant to work in the house, and forget she ever had a mind!

There were no women writers then, or poets, or painters, or teachers. No women in business in Palestine. Or in politics. Even in their own homes no lady was expected to have any thoughts of her own, except about the children she cared for, and the chores of homemaking.

"Did Jesus mean that homemaking wasn't important?" Martha asked herself as she poked at the coals under the copper kettle.

She shook her head, answering herself. No! Jesus knew, and she knew, that Mary did her share around the house. He knew, and honored, the work of women's hands. He meant only that there was more than that in the world for women!

"You know," said Martha to the hourglass that timed her cooking, "what He said out there in the garden is something completely new! It was as if Jesus were opening a door to all women and all girls—to ones not even born yet! As if He were pointing the way for the years ahead. Someday there will be many girls like Mary in the world!"

Then Martha laughed out loud. "But there will always be plenty like me!" she said. "The world needs us both!"

Then with a flurry and a scurry, Martha bustled back to work, bending over her pots and pans.

When the table was set, and the family gathered, Jesus gave thanks for the food they were about to eat. Tasting, He praised Martha's savory stew, and His eyes saw each detail of her work—her crisp linens, her shining dishes. And a blessing was in each look He gave her.

Across the table Mary met Martha's eyes. And the sisters smiled, for both knew they served Jesus, each in her own way.

Lazarus

OUT into the desert beyond the Jordan went Jesus and His disciples, far from the dangers of His enemies in Jerusalem. But Jesus was not hiding, and He did not keep His whereabouts a secret. The crowds who believed in Him found Him, and came to Him even there.

One night as Jesus preached by the light of a campfire a messenger on a donkey clattered across the rocks, weary and out of breath.

"I have come from Bethany, Master," he said. "Your friends, Mary and Martha, have sent me to tell You that Lazarus, their brother, whom You love, is sick!"

As he spoke, Jesus stared into the fire. For a moment He was silent. Then He thanked the messenger and told His disciples to give him food and shelter for the night.

Asked Philip: "Lord, will You go and heal Lazarus?"

Jesus shook His head. "This sickness is not unto death," He said, "but for the glory of God, that the Son of God may be glorified by it."

And that was all Jesus said about the matter.

The disciples peered at each other, and pulled their beards in puzzlement. That didn't sound like the Master! He would heal any stranger who asked, and believed. Yet now Lazarus, whom He really loved, was sick, and Jesus seemed hardly to care. Strange, indeed!

Then Thomas' face brightened. "He is afraid to go!" he whispered to the others. "He knows it is dangerous to go so near Jerusalem."

"Ah! Good thing He stays here! Sensible!" they said

among themselves. "To go back to Bethany, so near the city, would be like walking into the den of a bear. By now the Temple is so alarmed by Him they are surely planning to kill Him. Maybe kill us too! The Master is right. It is all very sad about Lazarus, of course—we all love Lazarus— but it is much wiser to stay here and be safe!"

How little they understood, these men so close to the heart of Jesus!

Then, suddenly, two days later, Jesus announced that He was going to Bethany.

"Why, Lord?" cried the disciples. "The last time we went near Jerusalem You were nearly stoned to death! Why go back?"

"Lazarus, our friend, sleeps. But I go that I may awake him out of sleep," said Jesus.

"Lord," protested the disciples, "if Lazarus sleeps, he shall do well!"

The smile faded from the lips of Jesus and He spoke to them sternly:

"Lazarus is dead!"

Heartbreaking, mournful news, that! But how did Jesus know?, they wondered. No messenger had come. And if Lazarus were dead, why should Jesus go—and run the risk of being killed Himself?

Then Jesus said an even stranger thing:

"Lazarus is dead. And I am glad, for your sakes, that I was not there—that you may believe. But let us go to him."

Then up spoke Thomas, whose other name was Didymus, which meant "the twin." Thomas, the hard-headed, the doubter, was certain that if Jesus went to Bethany His enemies would somehow kill Him. And Thomas wheeled on the others of the twelve and snapped:

"Let us go also, that we may die with Him."

And sad and fearful though they were, they agreed with Thomas, all of them, from John to Judas Iscariot. But not

one of them could understand why Jesus had not gone before, or why He was going now.

The house of Martha and Mary was crowded with mourners, friends and relatives weeping for Lazarus who was dead. As soon as she heard that Jesus was coming, Martha ran out to meet Him.

"Lord!" cried Martha, as she met Him at the edge of town. "If You had been here my brother would not have died!"

Her thin face was red with grief, and her cheeks quivered, but she bowed her head and said, "But now—also I know—whatever you will ask of God, God will give it to you."

Jesus put His warm, strong hand on her trembling shoulder and whispered: "Your brother shall rise again!"

Martha frowned, not daring to hope. Slowly she said, "I know that he shall rise again—in the resurrection at the last day."

Jesus cupped her chin in His hand, and made her eyes meet His, as He said:

"I am the resurrection and the life. He that believes in

Me, although he be dead, shall live. And everyone that lives and believes in Me, shall not die forever. Do you believe this?"

"Yes, Lord!" cried Martha. "I have believed that You are Christ the Son of the living God, Who are come into this world."

The look in His eyes comforted her, and released her. She gathered up her skirts and turning, rushed back to the house and called her sister Mary:

"The Master is come and calls for you."

Mary did not wait. She ran out of the house, down the stony hillside. Everybody in the house followed her, thinking perhaps she was going to the grave to weep. And they did not want her to go alone.

Mary did not care who was following. She wanted only to see Jesus, and when she found Him waiting where Martha had left Him, she fell on her knees at His feet and said as her sister had said:

"Lord, if You had been here, my brother would not have died!" Tears poured down Mary's cheeks, and all those who came with her were weeping too.

But Jesus said simply: "Where have you laid him?"

"Lord, come and see!" said her friends and relatives.

And Jesus wept.

Together they walked into the Bethany hills, and as they went, the people seeing the Master weep whispered:

"Look how much He loved Lazarus!"

"Ah, yes, but———" said one.

"But? But what?"

"He has opened the eyes of a man born blind. Couldn't He have caused this man He loved so much not to die?"

Now they were come to the grave of Lazarus. It was a sepulchre, a tomb like a cave, dug down out of the slant of a rocky hill. And the entrance was closed with a boulder.

Jesus said: "Take away the stone."

But Martha said to Him: "Lord, he has been dead four days. By this time . . ."

Jesus looked at her, and she fell silent. And He said, "Did I not say to you that if you believe, you shall see the glory of God?"

And when He said that, the relatives went to push away the stone. Sweating, gasping, and feeling they were doing a mad thing, they rolled it back. And Jesus, going to the edge of the tomb, looked up at the sky and spoke:

"Father, I give thanks that You have heard Me. And I know that You hear Me always, but because of the people who stand about have I said it—that they may believe You have sent Me."

There was a moment of silence. The spring winds blew sweetly on their faces, and the smell of the tomb was crossed with the odor of wild flowers.

Then Jesus cried in a loud voice:

"Lazarus! Come forth!"

And Lazarus came. Lazarus who had been dead and buried four days, came out of the tomb. He was wrapped in grave cloths, bound, hands and feet, by the white winding sheet, and his face was wrapped around with a napkin. But still, Lazarus came into the light of day, back from death to life.

Jesus said: "Loose him, and let him go."

And Lazarus embraced his sisters, and smiling and laughing and weeping with joy and wonder they knelt before the Master Who had said:

"I am the resurrection—and the life."

The Second Box of Ointment

IT was now the time of the Passover, the greatest of all celebrations in Israel.

From the sea and from the caravan roads of mountains and deserts, by ships and camels and walking barefoot, travelers by the thousands turned their faces to Jerusalem. This was the great Passover Feast in memory of the night centuries before when the Lord destroyed the first-born children of the Egyptians who had conquered the Jews, and passed over the houses of the children of Israel.

Everyone who could possibly do so wanted to go to the Temple in Jerusalem for the Passover Feast each year. For seven days they would join in the prayers, offering up the holy paschal lamb to God and eating the special unleavened bread.

Soft spring lay over the city, and the cuckoo sang and the new little flowers bloomed. But in the council room of the Pharisees and the high priests there was only cruelty and hate. These men had heard that Jesus had brought Lazarus back to life, and made him rise from the dead, and they were afraid.

"What will we do with this Jesus? He works many miracles, and the people love Him and believe in Him. And if we leave Him alone, soon everyone will believe in Him, and the Roman rulers will come to us and take away our jobs and our power and our wealth because we did not stop this One called Jesus!"

Caiphas, the high priest, stroked his long and perfumed beard. "You know nothing!" he said, with a scheming smile. "It is better for one Man to die, than for a whole nation. . . ."

And from that moment the chief priests and the Pharisees began to plot exactly when and where to kill Jesus. And they were sure their chance would come at Passover, when Jesus would come to Jerusalem.

Six days before the Passover, Jesus and the twelve came to Bethany, the town of Mary and Martha and Lazarus. But this time Jesus did not stay at their house, but in the home of a man called Simon the Leper—one of those healed by Jesus.

For the past weeks the disciples had grown steadily more frightened. They had heard whispers of the plots to kill Jesus when the Master came to Jerusalem. They had heard Jesus Himself tell them that He would suffer.

Jesus had said: "The Son of Man shall be betrayed to the chief priests and to the scribes and to the ancients. And they shall mock Him and spit on Him and scourge Him and kill Him. And the third day He shall rise again."

Terrifying words from the Master they loved!

Still, as the days passed, the disciples began to breathe easier. Jesus seemed neither worried nor alarmed. He was planning to go to Jerusalem, they said to themselves, and would He do that if there were really danger that He would be killed?

By the time they all sat for dinner together in Simon the Leper's house, the disciples had practically forgotten their fears. Martha, who was, after all, the best cook in town, served the dinner, an excellent dish of braised lamb and garden vegetables. And with them was Lazarus, eating as heartily and as happily as if he had never been buried for four days—living proof of the Master's power.

Mary, the other sister, was mysteriously absent.

Suddenly she came through the doorway and knelt at the feet of Jesus—just as years ago the red-haired woman in the Pharisee's house had done. In Mary's hands she carried an alabaster vase. In it was a pound of spikenard, a very expensive ointment. When Lazarus had died the sisters had bought this ointment for his burial, and had spent every penny of their savings for it.

Silence fell as the guests watched Mary.

She knelt and lifted one foot of Jesus and began to rub His instep and toes with the ointment. Then she took the other foot and rubbed it too with the sweet-smelling paste. And then, again like the other woman before her, she dried the Master's feet with her long dark hair.

Then Mary broke the alabaster jar and poured the rest of the ointment on the top of the Master's head and rubbed it in with strong, slender fingers. And the room was filled with the odor of the ointment.

Judas Iscariot could no longer be still. With a scowl and a sigh of impatience he whispered to Martha:

"What a waste of this ointment! It could have been sold for three hundred pence! It cost much more than that when you bought it for your brother Lazarus, who as things turned out, did not need its sweet smell. Your sister could have sold it all, and given it—uh—to the poor!"

And all at table, except Jesus Himself, began to mutter among themselves, and throw dark glances toward Mary. All twelve apostles, and Simon the Leper, even Lazarus, frowned at her with her extravagant alabaster vase in her hands. But the darkest glances of all came from Judas.

For a long time Judas Iscariot had been the treasurer of the apostles. He kept the purse, and handed out the money for the few things they needed to buy. But Judas cared more for the money than he did for Jesus, or for the poor. He was a thief at heart, and often he took the coins that were meant for the poor and kept them secretly. Judas would actually have snatched the alabaster box and what little was left of the ointment from Mary's hand, if Jesus had not spoken and stopped him.

"Let her alone," commanded Jesus, "that she may keep it against the day of My burial."

The apostles fell into shocked silence, and Jesus continued:

"Why do you trouble this woman? For she has wrought a good work upon Me. For the poor you have always with you, but Me you have not always.

"And she, in pouring this ointment upon My body, has done it for My burial.

"I say to you, wherever this Gospel shall be preached in the whole world, that also which she has done shall be told for a memory of her."

And indeed after nearly two thousand years, in which it has been told day after day, here it is being told again!

Palm Sunday

THE roads leading to Jerusalem were clotted with pilgrims, families from all parts of the world hurrying to celebrate the Passover Feast at the Temple. Inside the city the narrow cobblestoned streets were crowded with thousands upon thousands of other pilgrims who had already arrived.

One question filled the air, one question repeated over and over:

"Where is Jesus?"

In the bazaars, in the marketplaces, in the courts of the Temple, the people asked anxiously:

"Where is He? Isn't the Master coming to celebrate the feast with us?"

And in the dark council rooms of the Temple, the Pharisees and the chief priests who hated Jesus asked the same question, but for a different reason:

"Where is Jesus? We cannot destroy Him until we find Him! Is He afraid to come to Jerusalem?"

Jesus was on His way. As the sun climbed in the clear spring-blue sky that Sunday morning, He was walking with His twelve apostles, step by step nearer to the city.

The wind danced in the petals of the anemones, and whirled the shy green leaves of the olive trees. The world seemed new with that dawning, fresher and more lovely after the days of sodden chill rain. It was a day made for gaiety and song.

But the apostles, walking behind Jesus, wore long faces, and their eyes were dark-circled and sad. Only the night before, Jesus had spoken to them of His death, death that would strike Him in Jerusalem. They were afraid for Him, those twelve loving friends, and afraid for themselves.

"We will follow Him, even to death!" they said to each other. "But why does He insist on going headlong into danger? Why does He lead us to Jerusalem, instead of away from it?"

"And why—*why*—does He smile this morning?"

At the foot of that green Mount of Olives, in sight of Jerusalem's gates, Jesus paused. To Him He called two of His disciples, and with a mysterious smile He said:

"Go into the village that is over there, near you. And immediately as you come there you shall find a colt tied, upon which no man has yet sat. Loose him, and bring him here!"

Bring him here? Without paying for it? Or asking, Lord?

Before they spoke, Jesus answered them: "If any man

shall ask you: 'Why do you loose this colt?' you shall say
to him: 'Because the Lord has need of his service.' "

Obediently the disciples went, keeping their questions
to themselves. Down the last slope of the mountain, and
into the valley they hurried, and through the gates of the
nearest town.

There by the gate stood an ass, a farm beast used to
the yoke, and her baby colt, unbroken to the saddle. Three
men, the farmers who owned the beasts, lounged idly by.

More than a little nervously the two disciples went up
and unhitched the young donkey.

"Hey, there—what are you doing, untying that colt?"
asked one of the owners. "It's mine, you know!"

"The Lord has need of him," answered the disciples.

And that was enough! Without a question, without an
objection, the farmers smiled, "Take him!"

The disciples, grinning in fresh amazement at the mysteries of their Master, led the little white donkey by the
short tether of leather thongs, straight up the slope to Jesus.
And when the Master asked them, the disciples laid their
extra robes over the donkey's back for a makeshift saddle,
and the Master straddled him, and rode slowly down from
the mountain.

Following on foot they whispered to each other:

"Isn't it strange that after three years of traveling only
on foot He suddenly rides? Of course, He *should* ride—but
why suddenly now, and why on an ass?"

They did not find their answer then. But later they
were to understand. Then they would remember, as John
the Apostle tells in his Gospel, the words spoken centuries
before by the great prophet Zacharias, the words which had
described the coming of Christ:

"Rejoice greatly, O daughter of Sion, shout for joy, O
daughter of Jerusalem. Behold your King will come to you,

the just and saviour. He is poor, and riding upon an ass, and upon a colt, the foal of an ass."

Slowly Jesus rode, and they followed, down through the bleak Valley of Gehenna, and up the steep path to Jerusalem.

Then, a most extraordinary thing happened.

One moment Jesus and the twelve were traveling unnoticed and unattended. The next instant, they were the center of a singing, shouting, glorious crowd, the center of the greatest, happiest parade in history.

"There He is! There is Jesus!" cried a voice from the throngs. "See He rides on a white donkey like a king!"

One voice cried out, and thousands joined it. The pilgrims on the road, dusty and footsore, whirled to face Jesus with joy shining on their faces.

And in the city of Jerusalem the people heard that Jesus was coming, and they ran pell-mell to greet Him, and welcome Him.

"Hosannah!" they cried. "Blessed is He that comes in the name of the Lord!"

"Hosannah to the Son of David!"

Hundreds of thousands of people surged around Him, wild with devotion. They threw their robes and cloaks upon the stony ground to spread a carpet for Him to ride. From the trees they cut green boughs of sweet-smelling balsam, acacia, and tamarisk, and spread palms before Him. Running far ahead they strewed the ground with the shining fronds of palms, with bouquets and nosegays of wild flowers.

"Hallelujah! Glory to God!" they cried.

"Blessed be the King that comes in the name of the Lord."

"Peace in heaven and glory on high."

"Hosannah in the highest!"

They looked on Him with love and honor shining in

their eyes. Here was their King, their Savior, their Messiah, Son of God, Christ the Prince of Peace. Never did any conqueror ride in such triumph as the gentle-faced Jesus, King of all hearts.

Up the steep hill the procession climbed, up very near to the city with its long, curving walls of tawny stone, its tower forts and tall, armored gates.

And as Jesus came near to Jerusalem, tears sprang to His eyes. Jerusalem, golden city of the ages, where for thousands of years good and holy men had waited for this day when Jesus the Son of God would come—was also, He knew, the city where He would die, the home of those who would kill Him. And Jesus wept for Jerusalem.

On He moved with the joyous crowds, amid the singing and the shrill hallelujahs and the deep-toned amens. Through the city gate He rode, where mobs from the narrow streets came spilling and mingling, to join them, the whole city running to ask:

"Who is this?"

And the people answered: "This is Jesus, the prophet, from Nazareth of Galilee!"

The blind and the crippled, the sick and the deaf and the dumb clustered round Him and followed as closely as they could until He reached the courts of the Temple. And there in the shadow of the altar of the Most High, Jesus healed them.

From the shadowy pillars at the back of the Temple the Pharisees and the chief priests had watched in horror.

"He holds the crowds spellbound!" they said.

"The whole world has gone after Him, to follow Him like a king!"

"With those mobs He could do anything. He is a very dangerous Man, this Jesus," said Caiphas, the high priest. "We must stop Him. Destroy Him. Kill Him. Not now—but soon. Listen! Hear how they praise Him and salute Him and even adore Him. They are quoting the words of our prophets, and saying that He is the Savior!"

And, indeed, at that moment, children, flocking near the Master who loved them so dearly, were repeating the famous words of the prophets:

"Hosannah to the Son of David!"

The Son of David! That was another name for the Savior, a name from the Scriptures! And the sound of it terrified the Pharisees and the sadly unholy chief priests who feared and hated Jesus.

"Hosannah to the Son of David!" chanted the children, heaping bright flowers at the feet of Jesus, and singing with joy and love.

The Pharisees and the chief priests pushed their way through the crowds, angrily shoving the children aside.

"Do you hear what these brats are saying?" they screamed at Jesus.

"Yes!" agreed Jesus. And He too quoted from the Scriptures to them: "Have you never read: 'Out of the mouths of infants you have perfected praise?'"

Ah! They knew what that meant. That, too, was an old prophecy about the Messiah!

Back they went into the shadows, seething with anger.

"This Jesus must not live!" they whispered with venom. "He will destroy us all!"

And from the Temple still came the voices of the children, the children who were so much wiser, the children who knew and loved Jesus:

"Hosannah to the Son of David!"

"Hosannah—and glory to God!"

Trouble in the Temple

SO popular was Jesus, so beloved by the people, that His enemies were afraid to make a move against Him.

The rulers of the Temple, the chief priests and the Pharisees, clenched their fists and hissed into their beards, and muttered darkly. But day after day, that week before Passover, Jesus came into the Temple to teach and the crowds listened to Him with such devotion that no one dared interfere.

On Tuesday morning of that week, Jesus strode as usual into the Temple, flanked by His twelve apostles.

Inside the outer court Jesus stopped, the fire of indignation playing over His face.

On one side stood the tables of the money-changers. At those counters men must stop and change their everyday Roman coins into the coins of Israel, for only those coins could be used in the Temple. And it was not a fair exchange. The money-changers kept a fat sum for themselves, swelling their own pockets with the hard-earned cash of the poor.

Jesus looked at the clutter of pennies and mites, and gold and silver, and at the hard eyes and brass smiles of the greedy money-changers and His lips tightened. Who put those cheating money-changers in the Temple, and who shared in their thievery? The high priests and the Pharisees! Jesus knew.

On the other side of the court stood the booths and stalls of the men who sold animals for sacrifice at the altar, the chairs of the dove-sellers and the sheep-merchants. The good souls who came to the Temple believed that God appreciated the sacrifice of animals to Him, and according to their means they bought lambs or pigeons to offer Him, even as Joseph had done so long ago when Jesus was a baby. But animals in the Temple cost twice as much as they did elsewhere, and the poor were robbed when they tried to buy them.

Slowly Jesus moved through the throng of buyers and sellers, watching the money pass hands. He heard the cooing of the doves and the bleating of the young lambs, and the shrill voices of men bargaining.

Out of the corner of His eye Jesus watched the people going up to change their money at the bankers' tables. And in His hands, the apostles noticed, He carried a loop of ropes, picked up somewhere idly on His morning walk to the Temple.

Suddenly, swiftly, Jesus' hands moved. From those cords He made a whip, a scourge, and before anyone could see what He was going to do, He let fly with that whip.

He flailed the backs of the money-changers, and turned over their tables so that the money spilled and ran tinkling over the marble floor.

He whirled on the sellers of doves and lambs and knocked over their chairs and overturned their booths. The birds fluttered free, soaring and flapping and wheeling overhead, and the curly-haired lambs scampered and scattered and ran out of the gates of the Temple.

Startled and screaming the crowd backed away.

Alone Jesus stood. His breath came heavily, His face was damp, as He lifted His hands and said in a voice deep with scorn and anger:

"Is it not written: 'My house shall be called the house

of prayer to all nations'? But you have made it a den of thieves.

"Take these things hence, and make not the house of My Father a house of traffic!"

The money-changers and the dove-sellers scrambled to their feet and backed slowly out of the Temple, stumbling and pushing and falling as they went. And the doves soared overhead, clinging to the blood-red cedar beams of the ceiling.

Then one of the Pharisees, standing in the crowd, called out:

"By what right do You do these things? What sign do You show us, seeing that You do these things?"

Jesus turned His face to the Pharisee, but He answered in a voice that all could hear:

"Destroy this temple, and in three days I will raise it up."

The people looked at each other and smiled. How could anyone, even the Master do that?

"It took forty-six years to build the Temple!" they said. "And will You raise it up in three days?"

The Pharisees began to laugh, and jeer, and mock at Jesus. But the others in the crowd, who loved Him and believed Him, watched Him leave in silence.

They did not understand those words, either, but they remembered them. For they knew that Jesus had a way of clothing great secrets in strange words.

Jesus left the Temple, and went to His lodgings in Bethany, His apostles with Him.

And those who saw Him go pondered His words, and turned back into the Temple, the house of prayer, the house of God the Father.

The Last Supper

AT sundown on Thursday of that week, thirteen men met to celebrate the holy feast of Passover in a great gray hall, an upper room in a house on Mount Zion in Jerusalem.

It was a plain room, heavy-beamed and high ceilinged, furnished only with rattan divans and a long oaken table on which tall candles were burning. The flickering light cast long shadows of the apostles against the unwindowed walls.

During the afternoon the lamb they must eat for the Passover dinner had been prepared in the courts of the

Temple as was proper. Soon now they would eat it, when twilight brought the official beginning of the Passover feast.

Now they were all gathered in this room as by a kind of miracle. They had not known where to turn for the holy day, or where to go, until that afternoon the Master had called Peter and John, and said:

"Look, as you go into the city, there shall meet you a man carrying a pitcher of water. Follow him into the house where he enters. And you shall say to the good man of the house: 'The Master says to you, where is the guest chamber, where I may eat the Passover feast with My disciples?' And he will show you a large dining room, furnished. There you will make things ready."

Every word of which came true immediately. Now here they were, assembled in that same goodman's upper room, all twelve, waiting for the Master to come.

In spite of all that Jesus had foretold, none of them realized that this was to be their last meal together. It was a Jewish holy day, a holiday, and in spite of all their fears they were eager, and busy talking. And, because they were still a long way from being saints, they began an old argument.

"Which one of us is greater?" they asked. "Which one of us will be the closest to the Master in the glory of the future?"

Once before Jesus had rebuked them for such bickering. This time He answered not in words but in action.

In the midst of their argument He suddenly appeared, wrapped in a long blue cloak, at the doorway. They fell silent like children discovered in a squabble.

Laying aside His cloak, Jesus poured water from a pitcher into a basin. Then He knelt at the foot of His strongest and strangest disciple, Peter.

"Master!" gasped Peter. "Do You wash my feet? No! No! *You must not!*"

Jesus, on His knees, looked up at the great heavy-handed fisherman: "What I do, you know not now—but you shall know hereafter."

Peter's face turned deep red. "You shall never wash my feet!"

The Master's voice was calm: "If I wash you not, you shall have no part with Me."

Then Peter bowed his head and said: "Lord, not only my feet, but also my hands and my head."

Turning next to John, Jesus began to wash the feet of each of the twelve. Twenty-two feet He washed and dried, and at last He came to Judas Iscariot.

Some in the room had already noticed how strangely Judas was acting that evening. Tonight he seemed sad, and somehow apart from all the others. Pale and glassy-eyed he sat; his crown of stiff red curls and his wavy red beard made his eyes seem blacker and darker than ever, and he spoke not at all, not even when Jesus washed his feet.

Then the Master rose and said: "Know you what I have done to you? You call Me Master and Lord; and you say well, for so I am. If I then being your Lord and Master, have washed your feet, you also ought to wash one another's feet. Amen, amen I say to you: the servant is not greater than his lord. Neither is an apostle greater than He that sent him."

And there was the final answer to the question: Who is greatest in the kingdom of heaven? The one who humbles himself, and puts himself last, as Jesus did.

Then Jesus sat at the table surrounded by the twelve familiar faces.

His arms were opened, His hands lying, palms up, on the snowy cloth. His eyes were lowered and He looked at no one.

To His right sat the pale-faced John, his cheek almost touching the Master's shoulder. And farther to the right was

baldheaded Peter, absent-mindedly twiddling a knife between his horny thumbs. Near him, Andrew and Simon
Zelotes. To the left were bearded Matthew, and Jude Thaddeus, the oldest man at the Last Supper. Then came curly-
haired, black-bearded Thomas, and James the Greater, the
tall and powerful brother of John. Next to him was Philip
the gentle, and Nathanael Bartholomew, at the end of the
table with James the Lesser, Jesus's cousin. And finally, on
the opposite side, as if set apart from all others, sat Judas
Iscariot.

"I have desired to eat this Passover feast with you,
before I suffer," said Jesus. "For I say to you that from
this time I will not eat it, till it be fulfilled in the kingdom
of God."

After a long silence He lifted His voice in one of the
beloved old psalms of David, and all sang with Him, giving
glory to God. A cup of wine was passed and blessed. Then
each ate of the traditional foods of Passover. To each a por-
tion of the bitter herbs, endive and lettuce, dipped into a
compote of almonds, nuts and figs. As children these men
had learned that the color of those fruits was chosen to re-
mind them of the bricks which once in slavery in Egypt the
Jews had been forced to make without straw. And with the
bitter herbs they ate the ancient bread of misery, the mat-
zoth, the flat, nearly tasteless crackers that were all the Jews
had had to eat when they fled from the Pharaohs so long
ago. Then they ate the Passover lamb, roasted and savory.

Then Jesus said sadly:

"Amen, amen I say to you—one of you shall betray
Me."

Those sudden shocking words of the Master echoed
frighteningly in the dining room. This was the first time He
had ever said anything like that. Always He had seemed to
trust them all completely. One of them would *betray* Him?
Turn against Him in secret, sell Him out to His enemies,

cause His death? The idea stunned them. They *loved* Him! How could they betray Him?

Yet, humbly, their faces tight with sorrow, they asked Jesus one after another:

"Is it I?"

"Is it I, Lord?"

"Who is it?" shouted Peter, glaring around at them all.

And John, who loved Jesus deeply, whose head even then rested on Jesus' chest, asked: "Lord, who is it?"

"He it is to whom I shall reach bread dipped," Jesus answered. "He that dips his hand with Me in the dish, he shall betray Me."

They were like frozen men, unable to move, as the Master dipped a morsel of bread in the dish of lamb and gravy and then quietly held it out toward Judas.

The voice of Judas, the treasurer, trembled as he croaked:

"Is it I, Master?"

"You have said it," answered Jesus. Even then He could not keep the pity from His eyes. "That which you do, do quickly."

Judas took the morsel of bread and gravy, and then fled from the room. The door slammed heavily behind him.

Even then, the disciples did not really understand. True, Judas Iscariot was the least popular among them—but who could believe he would sell his Master's life?

As they looked at the door closing behind Judas, they told themselves that Judas must have simply been sent on an errand. After all, he was in charge of the purse and the money for them all. Perhaps Jesus had sent him off to buy supplies, or on some secret mission to give money to the poor.

And when Judas was gone from the candlelit upper room, Jesus did not mention him again.

Instead He turned their eyes to the most important,

most dramatic act of His life—so earthly simple, so heavenly in meaning.

He took bread, and blessed it, and broke it, and gave a piece to each of the eleven. And He said:

"Take you, and eat. This—is My Body."

And they ate.

Then He took the chalice, the cup, and filled it with wine, and gave thanks to God. And He passed the chalice of wine to the eleven, saying:

"Drink you all of this. For this is My Blood of the new testament, which shall be shed for many unto remission of sins."

And they all drank of it—all except Judas, who had gone, but who was still crouched on the stairway outside listening to the great new mystery—the way in which a man becomes one with God.

And Judas knew that for him it was too late.

This was the time of the real parting between Jesus and those who loved Him in this world, this hour after that first communion.

"Little children," He told them softly, "yet a little while I am with you. You shall seek Me, and as I said to the Jews: 'Where I go, you cannot come.' So I say to you now.

"A new commandment I give to you: That you love one another—as I have loved you, also love one another. By this shall all men know that you are My disciples, if you have love one for another."

But Peter cringed at the idea that Jesus was going away. And Peter said: "Lord, where do You go?"

Jesus answered: "Where I go, you cannot follow Me now. But you shall follow hereafter."

Urgently, lovingly, Peter cried, "Why cannot I follow You now? I will lay down my life—I will die, for You!"

Jesus looked at him, gently, but oh so sadly! "Will you

lay down your life for Me? Amen, amen I say to you, Peter, the cock shall not crow, till you deny Me three times!"

Peter roared in protest. Deny Jesus? Say he did not believe in the Master, did not even know Him? Never!

"Although I should die together with You, I will *not* deny You!"

Jesus raised His hand for silence, and motioned Peter and the others back to their seats. In a whisper He said:

"Let not your heart be troubled. You believe in God, believe also in Me.

"In My Father's house there are many mansions. If it were not so, I would have told you, because I go to prepare a place for you. And if I shall go, and prepare a place for you, I will come again, and will take you to Myself, that where I am, you also may be.

"And where I go, you know, and the way you know."

Thomas, of the black curls, leaned forward. "Lord, we do *not* know where You go—and how can we know the way?"

And Jesus answered, in words that men have been quoting ever since, for two thousand years:

"I am the way, and the truth, and the life. No man comes to the Father, but by Me. If you had known Me, you would without doubt have known My Father also, and from henceforth you shall know Him, and you have seen Him."

Words burst from Philip: "Lord—show us the Father, and it is enough for us!"

"Have I been so long a time with you," sighed Jesus, "and have you not known Me? Philip, he that sees Me, sees the Father also!"

There! In the simplest of words was the answer for which they had waited so long. Jesus, Son of Mary—Jesus of Nazareth—answered for them now:

"I am in the Father. And the Father is in Me."

He was in Himself God, one with the Father Almighty,

the Master of heaven and earth. At last He had told them the full, overpowering truth.

At that candlelit table in the upper room God sat with them now.

"If you shall ask Me anything in My name, that I will do.

"If you love Me, keep My commandments. . . .

"If anyone loves Me, he will keep My word, and My Father will love Him, and We will come to Him, and will make Our abode with him. . . ."

As the apostles fixed their eyes on Him in silence, Jesus made His farewell.

"Peace I leave with you. My peace I give to you. Not as the world gives, do I give to you. Let not your heart be troubled nor let it be afraid. . . .

"If you abide in Me, and My words abide in you, you shall ask whatever you will, and it shall be done unto you. . . .

"This is My commandment, that you love one another, as I have loved you. Greater love than this has no man, that a man lay down his life for his friends."

And as the candles burned low in their stands on the table of the Last Supper, Jesus rose and faced the darkness.

"Arise! Let us go!"

And one by one, they followed Him to Gethsemane.

Judas Iscariot

IT was a dark spring evening, damp and chill. It was the night of what we would call Thursday, the sixth day of April, in the Year of Our Lord 30.

In a firelit red-walled room near the Temple two men sat talking. One was Caiphas, high priest of the Temple, bitter enemy of Jesus. The other was Annas, father-in-law of Caiphas, and the most powerful man in Jerusalem.

For years Annas himself had been high priest of the Temple. Now that he was old, he had given the job to Caiphas, but everyone knew that Annas was still the real authority. Though he was over eighty, his cunning and his wisdom made him a man to be deeply feared. Like the others of those sad and selfish chief priests in the Temple Annas did not really love God. He loved no one but himself. That was the only unwise thing about him, and though he did not guess it, that was why he was also one of the unhappiest men alive.

Annas and Caiphas were met this night to plot the death of the Son of God.

Outside, the city of Jerusalem was filled with the noise of hundreds of thousands of pilgrims from all parts of the world, come to celebrate Passover. But inside the red-walled room all was quiet.

Annas, a long wisp of white hair dangling over the pale green glimmer of his left eye, sat by a fire of coals. Against

217

the high red wall across from him stood his son-in-law Caiphas, gorgeously dressed and young-looking behind his elab-
orate perfumed black beard.

Caiphas said: "I know it is late, Lord Annas, but my
business simply will *not* wait!"

Annas sucked his tooth, the only one left in his mouth
at his age. "What kind of business?" he asked.

"This is a most important night," said Caiphas. "Unless we settle this fellow Jesus, He will ruin us all. And tonight is the night to get Him."

Annas sneezed. "How can a wayside tramp ruin us?
That is all this Jesus is!"

Caiphas grinned. "The people believe that He is not a
tramp, but a prophet, or even the Messiah! They believe He
has a great new message. And that He can work miracles.
Last Sunday he rode into Jerusalem on a sleek white ass,
like a prophet—or a king—and the people swarmed out to
greet Him and sing Hosannahs!"

Annas waved an impatient hand. "That is dangerous,
true! But the people will forget Him soon. He can't really
be the Messiah, because there is no such thing! Let Him
preach and teach. What harm can He do? I am too tired to
worry about Jesus!"

Caiphas drew a deep breath. "My dear Lord Annas, He
has very dangerous ideas. He tells the people that all men
are equal in the sight of God. That God loves the poor, the
sinners, and the desperate as much—or maybe much more
than He loves us!"

"Well—this *is* news," muttered Annas over the fire.

"He wants every man to love his fellow man as a
brother—no matter who he is. He says that to be rich and
use your riches badly is a dangerous sin. He shakes His finger in *our* faces, and He is always telling the people that we
—all of us, Pharisees, scribes, chief priests and all—are
hypocrites, sinful men!"

Annas grunted and smiled to himself. "A terrible thing to let anyone say—because it is true!" he whispered.

Caiphas frowned. "The other day Jesus walked into the Temple with a whip and drove our money-changers and our dove-sellers out of the place!"

"He attacked our dealers?" croaked Annas. "But that is how we make our money! He can't be allowed to do that!"

"He said, 'Make not My Father's house a place of merchandise.'"

"*His* Father's house?" Annas pulled his short white beard. "That sounds like blasphemy! That sounds like He was saying He Himself is God!"

"Oh, and one thing more," said Caiphas with a triumphant smile. "He told the people there was no need for them to buy doves and lambs. He said God did not need such sacrifices at the altar. He said—listen, Annas!—that He Himself would be the sacrifice for their sins!"

"*Wah!*" rumbled Annas. "You are right, Caiphas. Jesus *is* dangerous. When the feast is over, we must go after Him."

"Lord Annas, we can't wait that long—not another day, even. The mobs might rise up and rescue Him. Jerusalem is full of people for the Passover."

"You have made definite plans, I suppose?" Annas asked.

"Everything is planned. We can be rid of Him quickly!" Caiphas rubbed his hands together with a smile.

Annas cocked his head, peering with his green eyes. "Caiphas—you don't suppose this Jesus has any real power to do miracles, of course? He couldn't just possibly be speaking the truth? He couldn't really *be* the Messiah?"

"Why do you joke with me, Lord Annas? There is no Messiah!"

"Of course." Annas stared into the orange and gray coals. "Tell me your plans!"

It would not be easy to be rid of Jesus. Most of the people of Jerusalem, the good souls who trusted Caiphas as their high priest, loved Jesus. And those who did not still would never sit by idly and see Him killed. No, Caiphas must find a way to make Him seem to be a criminal, and have Him executed as quietly as possible.

Swiftly Caiphas explained. They must arrest Jesus this night. They would accuse Him of blasphemy—of speaking against the true God, by pretending to be God Himself. And they would accuse Him of treason—of leading a revolution against the Roman conquerors, and trying to be King Himself. The punishment for those crimes was death.

"Blasphemy and treason," whispered Annas. "He has done neither. He is a good man, I am sure. But we have to say those things, or how else can we be rid of Him?"

Caiphas went on with his plan. "Now the judges who give Him a trial must be our own court, the Sanhedrin, the wisest judges there are. But we must have the trial at night —*this* night—because if the people hear that Jesus is in court there will be a riot, and they might kill us all. They love Him and want nothing to happen to Him!"

Only one thing was left, Caiphas explained. The judges of the Sanhedrin would sentence Jesus to death. But then the Roman governor, Pontius Pilate, must agree before Jesus could be executed. That was the law. The Romans were the conquerors, the real rulers, and nothing could be done without their approval.

"Lord Annas, you are the only man in Jerusalem who knows how to handle Pontius Pilate. Can you get him to agree to have Jesus executed? Quickly, before the crowds can save Him?"

The withered face of Annas flushed. "I will do it. Send out and arrest Jesus!"

Caiphas lifted his large, soft hands. "We don't know where to find Him, yet. But there is a man outside, one of

His own men, who wants to talk only to you, Lord Annas———"

"An informer? A traitor?"

"Yes. A man who was a friend of Jesus. He can tell us
where to catch Jesus tonight."

And Caiphas, going to the door, called softly:

"You may come in now—Judas Iscariot."

Judas slouched into the red-walled apartment. All his
life, in everything he did, there was an awkwardness in
Judas, and a roughness that gave him an uncouth swagger.
He was a red-bearded man with tough, curly hair, thick with
ringlets, and his eyes were always swollen. His straw sandals
squeaked on the marble floor as he bowed jerkily to Annas.

"Peace be with you," said Annas, in the usual greeting
of the time. "Your name, my son?"

"Judas, from Kerioth, so called Iscariot."

"How long have you been a friend of this Jesus?"

"I have been His friend for three years."

"How did it happen," asked Annas, "that a good man
like you took up with this wild Galilean?"

"I believed in Jesus," replied Judas.

"Believed what about Him?"

"Everything."

"Then why do you turn away from Him now, to betray
Him, and tell us where He will be tonight?"

"Understand me," exclaimed Judas. "I am not a com-
mon informer, or traitor. What I do, I do—and why is my af-
fair. But I do not want Jesus to come to harm!"

Annas remained silent.

"You will not hurt Jesus, will you?" asked Judas.

"The judges of the Sanhedrin will decide," said Caiphas from the corner.

"*Why* do you turn on Jesus now?" asked Annas again.

Judas stared at the ceiling. "How can I say? For a while

I believed Him, and all His words. He charms you, and the thoughts He puts into words sound wonderful. But these are violent times, and He talks soft words. If anybody slaps you on a cheek, turn your head around so he can slap the other one. Give in to everybody, He says. *Love* everybody. . . ."

"I think I see," interrupted Annas. "You thought He would be a leader of the people, maybe start a revolution against the Roman conquerors? Maybe become a king?"

"Yes!" said Judas. "He should have done that. He could have done that. He had His chance last Sunday when He rode into this city and the whole multitude practically fell at His feet."

"And if He had become King—you think you might have become pretty important yourself?" asked Annas.

Judas looked at the floor. "Jesus doesn't believe in money or power. For Himself—or for others."

"Now, Judas, one thing more. I believe you told the High Priest Caiphas that tonight was the best time to take Jesus. Why?"

"Because it is the only time He would let you take Him. Jesus could escape your guards, disappear before your very eyes if He had a mind to. I saw Him do that when the mob tried to kill Him in His home town of Nazareth. —But He expects to be taken tonight."

"And why no miracles tonight?" laughed Annas, who did not believe in miracles.

"Because He believes He must die. He keeps saying He must die to save the world. He will not resist you tonight," said Judas.

Annas suddenly stood up. "Listen to these special instructions. Find out for us where Jesus and the others will spend tonight. That is important—we must not arrest Him until Jerusalem is asleep. And we must be through with Him before Jerusalem wakes up."

"No harm will come to Him?" asked Judas again.

"Leave everything to us—and hurry."

"What I do, I must do quickly."

As Judas lifted his head, he heard a clink of silver. Annas was bent over, hands held near the flame of the candle. Judas saw that the old man was counting out money.

"I am not doing this for money!" Judas blurted out.

Old Annas glanced at him. "For money? For hire? Don't be foolish, Judas. You are doing it only because you think it is right. But I know no one does anything for nothing. You will be paid off now. Thirty pieces of silver!"

The coins clinked in the palm of Judas.

"Hurry!" said Annas. "Or you will be late."

Judas stalked out.

Annas also had to hurry. In the darkness of night in a litter chair he had himself carried through the streets past the Temple, to Pilate's castle.

Strange errand! Annas, who hated the Roman conquerors, and all Romans, must go to ask Governor Pontius Pilate, the Roman, for help. And Pilate, who hated the Jews he ruled, and despised them, would listen to wispy-haired Annas, who with his treachery controlled even the good men of Jerusalem, and help him. Annas was afraid of Jesus. Pilate was afraid of the mobs who might riot and get him into trouble with the Emperor in Rome. Two men, full of fear and hate, were to help each other on this darkest night of history.

Annas spoke to Pilate less than half an hour, but when he came out, he was triumphant.

"When the case of Jesus comes before Pilate, Jesus will die," he was thinking. "And that will be the end of it. Jesus will never be heard of again. And for His death, I and Pilate, we two, can take the credit."

Caiphas, too, had been busy. From the taverns and the back alleys he had called together a hired mob, thugs and jailbirds who would do exactly as Caiphas told them. At his command they would scream and shout and shake their fists, and insist that Jesus be killed. . . . It must appear that all Jerusalem was condemning the Man from Nazareth.

Caiphas had also assembled the Temple guards and some Roman soldiers with armor and swords, to make the arrest. The Temple guards had great dignity, but no weapons, because the Roman conquerors allowed them none. That was why the burly Roman soldiers were needed too.

"You have acted quickly, Caiphas," said Annas.

"Better than you realize," replied Caiphas. "I have sent word to every single member of the Sanhedrin, to every judge, telling them all that the Sanhedrin must meet tonight, secretly to dispose of Jesus.

"Meanwhile, Judas is back."

"Judas?"

"Judas Iscariot—the man who will take us to Jesus. He has learned exactly where to lead us."

"I do not like that man!" sniffed Annas. "I hate all traitors. But we must use him, hideous sallow-faced snake that he is."

And Judas, hated by the scoundrels he helped, started off into the darkness, leading the way to betray the only true Friend he had ever had.

The Dark Garden

IT was well after nine o'clock and quite dark when Judas, ready to betray his Master, came out the back doorway of the house of Annas, and into the alley. There the Temple guards and the Roman soldiers collected by the high priest Caiphas waited. They carried lanterns and torches, clubs and staves, and swords.

Judas turned his back on them, leading them around a corner into a jagged and poisonous-smelling little street. Not a sound was heard, except the shuffling feet of the men, the clank of armor, and the lonely howl of some faraway dog. Zig-zag through the streets they went. Pale in the light of spring stars loomed the Temple, and out through a gate they went, and down the steep hills.

Across the brook Kedron, Judas led them, and up toward the Mount of Olives.

The soldiers began to grumble.

"We have heard strange tales about this Jesus," they said. "They say He has mysterious powers. He can raise men from the dead, and walk on the sea, and feed thousands of people with only a few loaves and fishes. He is a Man to be afraid of!"

"He has never harmed anyone," said Judas.

"Where is He?"

"In a farm yard—a place where oil is pressed out of the olives. Some call it the Garden of Gethsemane," said Judas over his shoulder. "It is really a series of gardens, with walls. He has been there often, but never so late. Any other night He and His followers would be at the house of friends."

"What are they doing in the garden?" growled a wart-lipped soldier.

"I don't know. But there is nothing to fear. No one *could* fear Jesus!"

The thirty silver coins jingled in his bag as Judas sighed heavily and led the long column of men and hissing torches. Presently Judas called softly and lifted his hand, and they halted at a high hedge.

Now most of the party knew where they were. This was the farm yard with the oil press—a dark patch of olive trees, not far from the highroad to Bethany.

A little door-like opening had been cut in the hedge around the olive garden. Judas waved back the guards while he leaned in and peered. With narrowing eyes Judas searched among the gnarled and hunchbacked trees. His long, shrewish nose sniffed the soft orchard smell and the damp sweetness of night greenery. His peaked ears caught the deep sound of the wind, soughing and murmuring through those ancient olive boughs.

But where were the other eleven apostles and the Master?

Dimly Judas began to make them out.

Far off, in a different part of the Garden, he saw eight dark smudges of shadow under the trees. Those must be some of the apostles! And there, nearer to the hedge, in this part of the Garden, three more forms. That vast hunk of man sprawled on the grass, his head on a rolled-up cloak, was surely Peter, snoring. The slim form there by the pavilion was John, also deep in slumber. And that hulk under the biggest olive tree was James—John's brother, of course. They were all asleep.

But where was Jesus? Judas could not see Him.

Judas would have entered then and brought the guards with him, but he was stopped by the sound of a familiar voice at prayer. He stood listening. Somewhere off in the deeper greenery there, where he remembered a white boulder half buried in the earth, Jesus of Nazareth was on His knees. Judas could hear the suffering voice:

"My Father! If it be possible, let this chalice pass from Me!"

Judas twisted his nose in scorn. "Afraid?" he murmured. "He is afraid! He is praying to be let off—to escape——"

But Jesus was not through with His prayer.

"Nevertheless," prayed Jesus, "not as I will, but as You will!"

Then Judas was startled, because of that prayer in Gethsemane. The Master wanted not to die—yet if the Father insisted, knowing what was best, then He would obediently take death. What a way to pray! thought Judas. Such humbleness could not be right for a man. Most men prayed to tell God what they wanted, to strike a bargain with God. But not Jesus. Instead of forcing His will, He seemed to try to understand God's will so that He might obey it.

The silence after the prayer was touched by a low, swishing sound as of a trailing robe brushing the grass. Out of the dark and walking by starlight, the white figure of Jesus appeared, moving toward a sleeping disciple. Judas could see Him clearly now—tall, robed, walking barefoot across the chilly field. Jesus bent over the snoring man.

"Peter! What? Could you not watch one hour with Me? Watch you and pray that you enter not into temptation. The spirit indeed is willing but the flesh is weak . . . Sleep, now, and take rest. It is enough! The hour is come! Look, the Son of Man shall be betrayed into the hands of sinners. Rise up. Let us go. He that will destroy Me is at hand."

Then Jesus reached forward His foot and with the bare

toes gently joggled Peter's shoulder. The fisherman grunted, rolled over, then sat up violently.

"It is enough, Peter. The hour has come," Jesus said simply.

Peter scrambled to his feet and bared his knife.

Judas waited for no more. He laid a hard damp hand on the wrist of the leader of the soldiers and whispered:

"Now is the time. Let us go in and take Him. You will know Him sure. He will be the One I will kiss!"

The sound of rough voices and the clank of steel, the sight of the fires, brought all the sleepy disciples to their feet. They blinked at the frightening torch-lit scene, shining with cold brilliance of armor and swords.

Judas strode forward until he stood directly in front of Jesus.

"Hail, Master!"

Jesus moved toward Judas and seized him by the shoulders.

"Friend," said the Master sadly. "Whereto are you come?"

Then the arms of Christ drew Judas to Him, and the disciple kissed the Master on the cheek.

At the signal the Roman soldiers came forward, weapons in hand. But Jesus did not at once let Judas go. He held him tightly, His cheek laid against the tough ringlets, eyes lifted, as if asking a favor of the invisible. Then at last He released him, and as Judas stood back, Jesus the prisoner brought His hands together, and held them out as He approached the Roman captain.

That was more than Peter could bear. His fishing knife, a knife with a blade five inches long, gleamed in his hand. And Peter leaped at the officer. A moment's tussle, a disorderly struggle, and then the voice of Jesus:

"Peter! Peter! Put up your sword. . . . Do you think I cannot ask My Father, and He will give Me at once more than twelve legions of angels? How then shall the Scriptures be fulfilled?—for this is the way it must be done."

A little soldier from the Temple scurried forward with a handful of ropes and began to tie the wrists of Jesus. And seeing that, fear overwhelmed the disciples.

This sudden invasion of men in armor and others with cudgels and staves filled them with fright. The torches blazed and fumed. Voices rose in brawling question. Peter and all the others could take no more. Stampeded, like wild creatures, they scampered off into the night. Leaping the hedges and running as fast as legs could carry them, they left Jesus, the captive, alone.

He had done nothing to save Himself.

And as Judas, skulking in the flickering shadows, watched the Master bound, he remembered the strange, humble words of Christ's prayer:

"Lord, not My will, but Thine, be done."

The Trial

ANNAS, most powerful man in Israel, sat in his chair of state to await the Prisoner. The door flung open. The captain of the guard stood at attention.

"Lord Annas," he said. "Here as you commanded is the prisoner—Jesus of Nazareth!"

Rough hands shoved Jesus into the room, under the circle of light from the hanging candelabrum.

That first glimpse of Jesus jolted Annas like a blow to the heart. He had heard so much about this trouble-maker, and never before had seen Him. And one question pounded in the old man's mind. What was there about this tall Man in the white robe and sandals that seemed *so* different?

Outwardly He seemed quite ordinary. Like all poor men He wore His hair long, under a white turban. His beard was untrimmed. His clothes were plain. Except for His seamless inner robe of blue, He wore the usual garments.

What was it about Jesus? Annas wondered. Was it in the bright glory of His large calm eyes, set so wide apart? They spoke of God, those eyes—of the nearness and goodness of God. They were alive with power—and with love! Annas looked into those eyes and shivered. This Jesus—this prisoner with bound hands—was looking at him with *pity* in His gaze!

Annas cleared his throat, and straightened his withered old body. No one could pity him! He would show Jesus how important a person he was in Jerusalem!

"Jesus, You are called a blasphemer!" snapped Annas.

"Are You a blasphemer? Do You speak evilly and disrespect-fully of God?"

Jesus smiled calmly. "I have spoken openly to the world. I have always taught in the synagogue, and in the Temple, where all the Jews gather. And in secret I have spoken nothing. Why do you ask Me? Ask them who heard Me!"

Annas nodded. "I see. Very well, Jesus of Nazareth. I hold You for trial, immediate trial. The charge is blas-phemy. The punishment—death!"

They led Jesus directly to the home of the high priest, Caiphas, next to the Temple. Through the narrow dark de-serted streets the soldiers hurried Him. Outside Caiphas' front door they waited for orders.

Around Jesus surged an evil-faced mob, villains of the streets, hired by Caiphas for his own dark purposes. Jesus stood, hands bound, unmoving between His guards, never turning His head. Had He looked left, Jesus might have seen Peter, warming his tough old hands nervously over a coal fire, trying to remain hidden in the crowd. Had He looked to the right, He might have seen the young and distressed face of John. But the Master did not turn His head.

Peter was still warming his hands when a young woman carrying a bucket stopped suddenly before him. The girl's name was Huldah, and she was a servant of Caiphas' house. She studied Peter's face.

"You!" she said. "You were also with Jesus, the Gali-lean."

"I don't know what you are saying," lied Peter uneasily.

"You *were* with Him," Huldah insisted.

"Woman, I know Him not," said Peter. He moved off, hoping to lose himself in the crowd, fearful that the soldiers might hear the girl, and perhaps arrest him too.

But before he could go two steps another maid joined Huldah, crying: "Surely he is one of them. He is from Galilee. You can tell by his accent."

Then Peter swore: "I do not know this Man you are talking about."

The third lie had just left his lips when over the clamor of voices Peter heard the shrill crowing of a cock. Only a few hours before, at the Last Supper, Jesus had told him that before the cock crowed Peter would deny Him three times! And Peter had vowed he would never deny his Lord.

Peter turned and looked into the eyes of Jesus across the room. And the Lord's eyes were filled not with anger but with loving compassion. Jesus understood how weak men are, even those closest to Him, like Peter, whom He had chosen for such great work.

Jesus loved him still! And Peter wept bitter tears.

The Prisoner was kept waiting outside the Hall of Judgment where the trial would be held.

Inside hundreds of oil-burning torches set in niches in the walls lit the enormous auditorium. By eleven o'clock that Thursday night, most of the seventy judges were already in their places, called there by the high priest Caiphas. Turbaned, barefoot, and cross-legged, they sat on embroidered cushions. Nearby were the scribes, with inkhorns, quills, and parchment, ready to record all that was said. In the back were rows of younger men, who some day would become judges. These men, all of them, made up the Sanhedrin, which was the great Jewish court of law.

Learned men and wise, they took their role as judges seriously. They understood that it was their sacred duty to judge wisely, and mercifully, and honor the truth—and never to convict an innocent man.

The drone and buzz of their voices echoed in the great

hall, as the judges asked each other what emergency had led
Caiphas to call them at this hour. It was almost midnight!
They had all heard of this Jesus, of course, even though
very few had ever bothered to go to see Him or hear Him.
They thought Him harmless. What crime could He have
committed to summon them from their warm beds? They
did not know that Annas and Caiphas, whom they trusted,
were planning to trick them, to stampede them into condemning the most innocent of men.

Annas, wispy-haired and tiny, took his seat. Caiphas,
tall and gorgeous in his official robes, strode forward. The
trial could begin. Wheeling toward the great doorway Caiphas called out:

"Jesus of Nazareth, stand forth!"

It was just a few minutes past midnight when Jesus
stepped into the courtroom between His two guards.

"Let every man know that Jesus of Nazareth is accused of blasphemy," said Caiphas. "We will prove Him
guilty. Let the witnesses be called."

But the witnesses were most unimpressive.

"I heard this Man say: 'I will destroy this Temple that
is made with hands, and in three days I will build another
not made with hands,'" said the first witness, a tall, gaunt,
hungry man.

The second witness was a round little man, a merchant
in beans and barley.

"I heard Him say: 'Destroy this Temple, and in three
days I will raise it up.'"

On their embroidered cushions the judges grew rest-
less. They trusted and respected Annas and Caiphas. They
believed they were exactly what they pretended to be, holy
and wise men, representing all good and holy Jews. But
something strange was happening here.

Now Jesus had two friends in this court, two men who

knew and honored Him. One was Nicodemus, who once had come secretly to Jesus by night, to learn about the kingdom of God. Suddenly Nicodemus rose:

"Lord Caiphas—this is a stupid trial—ridiculous! Your witnesses do not agree. And even if they did, there is nothing they say that means that Jesus should be put to death. I say—put an end to this nonsense, and let us go home—and set Jesus free!"

The other judges nodded their heads.

Then Joseph of Arimathea got to his feet. "Lord Caiphas," he said. "You accuse Jesus of many things—but you cannot prove that He is guilty of any crime. It is already an hour past midnight. It is an insult to the dignity of this court to sit here trying to convict an innocent Man!"

Swiftly Annas whispered in the high priest's ear. Then Caiphas rose, in his blue and golden turban, and his robe embroidered with crimson pomegranates, and faced the court. And his smile was crafty and cruel.

You do not believe Jesus is a blasphemer?, he seemed to say. He has stayed silent—but He will never fail to answer now! Let Him convict Himself!

"Jesus of Nazareth," cried Caiphas. "I adjure You by the Living God, by the Almighty, that You tell us if You be the Christ, the Son of God."

Jesus' reply rang clear and loud: "You say that I am!"

And in the way of speaking of those times, the judges understood that Jesus meant: Yes!

Again Caiphas challenged Him: "Jesus of Nazareth, I adjure You by the Sabaoth—the numberless armies of angels—by the gracious and merciful God that You tell us if You are the Christ."

Again the crystal-clear voice: "You have said!"

And in the way of speaking of those days, Jesus was replying simply: Yes!

"Jesus of Nazareth, I adjure You by the long-suffering

and compassionate God that You tell us if You be the Son of God!"

Then Jesus answered so men of all ages should not doubt:

"*I am!*"

Caiphas himself turned pale. It was as if lightning had struck the court. Jesus had needed no witnesses—He had convicted Himself. For who could believe a carpenter from Nazareth was truly the Christ? Not these judges! Like many others, they expected the Messiah to come in glory like an earthly king. They were honestly horrified to hear this poor, barefoot wanderer from a small town call Himself the Son of God. For any mere man to do that was by their law a crime punishable by death.

"He has blasphemed! Behold, now you have heard!" Caiphas cried. Then wheeling to face the judges, he asked in a husky whisper: "*What think you?*"

From most of the scribes and priests and elders came a shout:

"He is guilty! We ourselves have heard it from His own mouth. He is guilty—and must die!"

Instantly Caiphas put them to the vote. One by one the judges must rise, and answer to his name, and vote whether Jesus must die. There were only two No's, from Nicodemus, and from Joseph of Arimathea. For the rest, each one of the seventy voted Yea.

In the midst of the solemn voting a man rushed down the great stairs, straight at Caiphas. In his right hand he held up a bag.

"Judas Iscariot!" cried Caiphas. "What do you here?"

"I declare," cried Judas, "that this Man you have condemned to death is innocent. You promised me you would not harm Him. Here is your money!"

And Judas cast his bag on the floor, and the pieces of silver rang sharply on the stone slabs and scattered, gleam-

ing like little living things in all directions. One rolled to the
heel of Annas.

"Judas, get you gone!" cried Caiphas. "Guards!"

"High priest," cried Judas. "I repent of what I have
done. I have sinned—and betrayed innocent blood."

In the silence that followed, Judas turned agonized eyes
on Jesus. But several judges called to him.

"What is your mistake to us?"

"Look you to it!" answered another.

From the throat of the lost apostle came a broken cry.
He rushed up the steps and out of the Hall of Hewn Stones
and the crowd parted to let him pass into the deepest darkness of the morning hours. Fleeing, where no man pursued
him, Judas rushed into an open field where he found a rope
and a tree. And there he hanged himself. . . .

Meanwhile, the voting continued, and soon was finished. The vote was death.

In the dark and early chill of Friday, April 7, Governor Pontius Pilate was waiting for Annas and Caiphas,
and their Prisoner. The air of the house before dawn was
damp and cold as a dog's nose. Pilate shivered as suddenly
he heard a tantara sounded on a horn.

The Prisoner was at the gate.

Pilate went to the balcony, and took his place on the
chair of ivory and bronze. Below him on the steps waited
Annas and Caiphas, and Jesus of Nazareth.

The Prisoner's face was blotched and bruised. His
beautiful seamless robe was spotted and stained with spit
from the mouths of soldiers. His hands, held before Him,
were still knotted at the wrists. And behind Him and
around Him stood the hired mob, muttering hurlyburly villains paid by Caiphas to frighten Pilate.

Swiftly Caiphas explained the case. This Jesus claimed
to be Christ the King. He had been condemned to death by

the Sanhedrin. Now the Roman Governor must also sentence Him to death, for the Jews by themselves had no legal powers.

Pilate turned to the accused and suddenly roared: "Are You the King of the Jews?"

Jesus answered calmly: "You say it."

Pilate looked down at Jesus, carefully searching His face. Something in those dark luminous eyes spoke to him, some power, some ray of love. And Pilate knew that un-

usual as it was, he must speak with Jesus alone. Brusquely
he ordered Jesus inside, where none could overhear.

He gave the Prisoner a chair, and leaning forward Pilate asked: "Are You really—the King of the Jews?"

Before Jesus could answer, they were interrupted. A
soldier, saluting, brought the governor a letter from his wife,
Procula—a strange, perfumed note.

"Have nothing to do with that righteous Man,"
scrawled Procula. "I have suffered many things this day,
and dreamed a dream because of Him."

Pilate scowled. No woman—not even his wife—could
tell him what to do! This was an important case. The Man
was charged with wanting to overthrow the Roman Empire
itself—with being a traitor, a revolutionary, a would-be
king.

Pilate repeated: "Are You the King of the Jews?"

Jesus leaned forward quietly. "My kingdom is not of
this world."

"But—have You a kingdom, then? *Are* you a king?"

"You say that I am a king!" smiled Jesus. "To this
end was I born, and for this cause I came into the world,
that I should bear witness to the truth. Everyone that is of
truth hears My voice."

And Pilate, hearing His voice, feeling the presence of
some mystery for which he had searched all his life, whispered: "What is truth?" And he read the answer in Jesus'
eyes.

Pilate leaped to his feet. "Do You not hear the terri-
ble things they say about You? Do You answer nothing?
Don't You know I have the power to crucify You—or to set
You free?"

Jesus answered: "You should not have any power
against Me unless it were given to you from above. He that
delivered Me to you has the greater sin."

Pilate's eyes gleamed. This Man understood! Why He

even forgave! And Pilate would do anything for a Man like that! He would try to save Him.

Past the torches of the guards they marched, Pilate and Jesus, to face the high priests and the mocking, jeering crowd. Defiantly, Pilate announced:

"I find no cause in this Man! No evil to condemn Him for. Set Him free!"

The crowd, the men Caiphas had hired to demand Jesus' death, went wild with anger.

"You must not set Him free! He is dangerous—He stirs up the people in Galilee," gasped Caiphas, "and then——"

"In Galilee?" Pilate grinned. Here was a way out for him! "If He is from Galilee I cannot judge Him! You must take Him to Herod, the ruler of Galilee!"

Annas grumbled and Caiphas roared, and his mob roared as he had paid them to do, but it was no use. Pilate closed his gates on them, glad to be rid of the problem of Jesus.

He was not rid of it long.

They took Jesus to Herod, as Pilate had commanded. This Herod, the same who had beheaded John the Baptist, was indeed ruler of Galilee. But this night he was staying in the ancient Jerusalem castle of his family, just opposite the Temple. And this night, too, he was feasting and drinking, more than any man should drink of wine.

Herod was too drunk to understand. He belched and hiccupped and cackled with laughter.

"King of the Jews? That's what He says He is?" giggled the fat, slovenly Herod. "Then dress Him as a king!"

A fine white robe Herod put on Jesus, the robe of a king. But judge Him? Never!

"Take Him back to Pilate!" roared Herod.

And the captive Jesus was led out the gate in the white

robe of mockery, the drunken jest of a worthless king against Him who is the King of Kings.

Back again across the city to Pilate's castle they led Jesus. Whatever crimes He had committed were done in Jerusalem—and Pilate could not escape deciding what to do with this Man. Once more the Governor sat facing the high priests, and Jesus, and the evil mob. Once more he tried to save Jesus.

"I have examined Him and find Him innocent. I will chastise Him, yes—but then I shall release Him."

Release Him! A yawp of fury came from the mob. Caiphas turned quickly and spoke two words to a man near him, a hired leader of these cutthroats. And from Caiphas' mouth the words ran to the core of the mob and there rose a sudden piercing cry:

"Crucify Him!"

From one, then from a dozen came the uncouth cry. Soon it was a rhythm and a chant—"Crucify Him! Crucify Him!"

Pilate shuddered. If this crowd were to riot, to attack him, the danger was great. Fear ran through him.

He rose and spoke directly to the people.

In Jerusalem, he reminded them, there was an old custom, that on the Feast of Passover the Governor could set one prisoner free. Now, said Pilate, we have another prisoner, the famous revolutionary leader named Barabbas, a murderer, who surely deserved to die.

"Whom shall I release to you—Barabbas, or Jesus Christ?"

Caiphas signaled. The crowd screamed:

"Away with this Man. Set Barabbas free!"

Arms outstretched, Pilate tried to plead with them, but they drowned out his words, and screamed:

"Crucify Him!"

Pilate raised his hand furiously for silence. "What evil has this Man done?"

Instantly the bitter, well-paid reply:

"Crucify Him!"

Pilate flung himself into the ivory chair. He gave an exhausted growl and made a sign. The guards took Jesus and stripped Him and beat Him with a whip, scourged Him till He barely had strength to stand.

Then they covered His bleeding back again with His own robe. On His head they pressed a crown of thorns, plaited by two idle soldiers of thorns from the hedges. And they led Him back to Pilate.

"Behold," cried Pilate. "I bring Him forth to you that you may know I find no evil in Him."

The crowd stared at the beaten Jesus, face and hands bloody, but standing straight and serene, with even more dignity than before.

"Crucify Him!" screamed the crowd.

And Pilate, defeated, afraid to protest again, screamed back at them: "Take Him, you, and crucify Him, for I find no evil in Him."

Turning, he called for a basin, a golden bowl of water, such as the Jews themselves used to wash away their sins. In front of them all, he, a Roman, washed his hands. And the coward who was afraid to set Jesus free, cried out for all to hear:

"I am innocent of the blood of this just Man."

The long trial was over at last. Jesus was condemned to be crucified, all very legally by Pilate.

And in the shadows of the wall a woman in a dark blue cloak stood weeping.

Mary had seen her Son. She had seen it all.

The Crucifixion

THERE was no true dawn that Friday, only a pale yellow creeping into the east slowly taking the place of the pale rose of sunrise.

From the guardroom of the castle of Pilate, Jesus descended the broad stairs in the light of the strange new day.

At the bottom of the steps the cross was waiting. It was a crude thing of wood, blackened and smelling of creosote and tar, the centerpiece rounded and large as the mast of a small ship, and the horizontal bar of a long beam split in half and fixed firmly with two bolted iron clamps.

At the soldiers' orders, Jesus knelt in the street. Part of the crossbar was hooked over His shoulder. Then He must stand with the weight of the cross on His back, and carry it Himself to the place of execution. He must drag it through the stinking, festering streets, never to pause, never to catch His breath. He was not alone in His punishment. Two thieves shared His fate, carrying their crosses in the same death march, strange company for the One Who took nothing but gave all.

Then suddenly, in a narrow part of the street, where today there is a broken stone wall, Jesus tottered, swayed, and fell. Weak He was from the scourging, and the cross was heavy, but the soldiers drew Him to His feet again and forced Him on.

Only a few minutes later Jesus saw in the crowd lining the street the face of His mother. Mary was watching there, by a blind alley that was filled with wretched poor children who clung to her skirts. The eyes of mother and

Son met, and all the years were in their glances. Then she was lost to His sight as the howling ragged mob closed around Him.

Dizziness came over Him once more. He was about to fall again. A murmur ran through the guards. Someone must help Him, or this Man would never reach the hill of crucifixion. But it was not for soldiers to carry a cross. Nearby stood a man named Simon, a pilgrim from the city of Cyrene in Africa, come to Jerusalem with his two small sons, Rufus and Alexander. Suddenly a guard pointed a finger, snarled an order.

"You there! Carry that Man's cross. Get on with it!"

Simon bent to help Jesus carry His cross, his two little boys following him in tears. He had done no crime. It was an aching nuisance to take such a load. But Simon did not refuse. And because of that half hour's toil, the world has never forgotten him. Simon, a stranger, and Simon alone, helped Jesus, when all His friends had run away.

Now as Simon moved onward with Jesus, the noise of the crowd took a different note. The city was awakening. News of what had happened to Jesus flew from doorstep to upper window and along the domed rooftops. The women heard it first, and they came running to see if it were true.

Through the gate Jesus passed, out into open country, within view of the gloomy hill. There the women of Jerusalem surged into the road, elbowing aside tramps and drunkards and all the savage crew that followed the cross. Unafraid, these housewives, daughters, and widows fought their way to the Master's side, weeping for Him.

Jesus' face took on new strength as He called to these women:

"Daughters of Jerusalem! Weep not over Me, but weep for yourselves and for your children." And with panting breath He warned them of the misery and destruction that would come to the city, before long.

Then, exhausted, even with Simon's help, He fell. And for the third time the soldiers drove Him to His feet. The end of their journey was at hand. He had only to carry the cross up that final stretch of steep hill.

Calvary, that hill! Golgotha, the natives called it, meaning the place of the skull.

It was noon as workmen arranged the crosses on the ground.

The three prisoners stood together—Dysmas and Ges-

tas, the two thieves—and Jesus. The soldiers shoved back
the crowd and the laborers laid three crosses near the three
new holes in the earth.

High noon, and the sun shone brightly on bay trees
and laurel, but on the four edges of the world clouds were
gathering. Few noticed the dark ring in the lower part of
the sky.

The guards stretched Jesus on the cross. They hammered huge pointed spikes through His palms to the cross-piece—then nailed His feet to the main piece. Then they hoisted the cross high, and dumped the base of it into the open hole.

There, at last, Jesus was crucified between two thieves. The three gaunt crosses stood in bleak silhouette against the paling sky.

On the cross over the head of Jesus, at Pilate's orders, they nailed a sign, written in three languages: Latin, Greek, and Aramaic, which was the language spoken in Jerusalem:

"Jesus of Nazareth, the King of the Jews!"

On the hill of Calvary the crowd of watchers grew minute by minute. The soldiers were there, and the ruffians, noisy and careless. The women were there, their faces pale with sadness and horror, and beside them the men, their eyes full of question and doubt. If the court, and Pontius Pilate as well, had condemned this Man, who were they to challenge it? They stood silent before the shouts of the soldiers, and they dared not look on His face.

Jesus turning from their faces murmured to the sky:

"Father, forgive them, for they know not what they do."

Forgive them? All? Where were His friends? Where are you, Peter? Where is John, the well-beloved, John who at our Last Supper laid his head on My breast and wept? Where is John now? And Judas! Judas is in the potter's field, after hanging from a tree. Is that what is to be seen so far, far off on the road to Bethlehem, where Mary's Son was born?

And all the others, where are they? Why did you run away, James and Thomas and Bartholomew and all the rest of you? For your lives you ran, scampering off in the dark rows of olive trees in the Garden of Gethsemane, scattering down the road to home. Why did you forsake Me? Because you feared you too would share this fate. You, too, might bleed and die. But the day is almost here when you will have such faith that fear will no longer matter.

"I thirst," said Jesus.

The soldiers grinned. They made Him a drink—a cup of wine mixed with bitter myrrh and gall and bile. He would not drink it. His last cup on earth was the chalice of the communion at the Last Supper.

At the foot of His cross the Roman guards who had nailed Him there threw dice for His robe which was without seam. They had taken all His garments and divided them into four parts—one for each soldier. But that beautiful seamless robe they did not tear. They gambled for it, instead.

While they threw the dice Jesus looked down and saw that He was not alone. Moving slowly through the crowd, ever closer to the cross, were three women—three Marys close at hand. Mary, His mother, stood at the foot of the cross. And Mary, the wife of Cleophas, His mother's sister, knelt beside her. Mary of Magdalen, out of whom He had once cast seven devils, lay prostrate on the earth.

And who was standing beside His blessed mother? John! John, the well-beloved disciple.

Jesus called out:

"Woman, behold your Son!"

Then turning to John, the drops of sweat glistening on His neck and forehead and cheeks, He said:

"Behold your mother!" And from that day on John would be like another son to Mary. But his love was a symbol of a greater service, for Jesus had spoken to mankind, had showed all living the glory of her motherhood.

The sky was darkening, slowly turning from deep violet-blue to black.

And the high priests came to mock Him:

"He saved others. Let Him save Himself if He be Christ. Save Yourself! Come down from the cross!"

Caiphas, standing with Annas, said out of the side of his mouth, "Others He saved. Himself He cannot save. He trusted in God. Let Him now deliver Him!"

But there were some who noticed that as the darkness deepened a small light shone behind His head.

One of the robbers, Gestas, took up the cry and spitting he said: "If You be the Christ, save Yourself—and us!"

But Dysmas, the thief on the right-hand cross, called back to him: "Neither do you fear God, seeing that you are under the same condemnation. And we are justly punished. But this Man has done no evil."

Then turning his head to the Master, Dysmas said with pleading sweetness: "Lord, remember me when You shall come into Your Kingdom."

Jesus opened His eyes, and through the blood and sweat He smiled, and spoke in His old clear, strong voice:

"So be it. I say to you—this day you shall be with Me in Paradise."

The storm was gathering its darkness now. The air was black and murky. There was a low roll of thunder, swelling to roar and crash over the heads of the people. And they began to fear. This was no ordinary storm. This was a brooding, deepening, lightless storm of sinister intensity.

It was close upon three o'clock in the afternoon, when for the fourth time they heard Jesus speak:

"My God, My God, why have You forsaken Me?"

Standing near the cross, Caiphas chuckled hoarsely.

"Hear that, Lord Annas? First He says He is God—then He asks Himself why He has forsaken Himself? That proves He's not God!"

The voice of Annas was low, and sad. "Do you not know your Scriptures, Caiphas? The Twenty-Second Psalm, have you not read it? It begins with those same words. And it tells what happened here today—every bit of it. King David wrote that psalm, predicting exactly this moment."

Jesus let them pour vinegar down His parched throat, vinegar from a sponge for His thirst. Then He spoke again:

"It is consummated."

And even Caiphas knew what that meant. Everything the prophets of the Old Testament had ever said had been fulfilled. Jesus was in truth the Messiah!

Then Jesus took a deep breath and spoke out softly, spoke as Mary remembered He would often speak when He was a boy, falling off to sleep on His bed in Nazareth —softly, and with a tone of surrender and relief:

"Father, into Your hands I commend My spirit."

And bowing His head, He died, about three o'clock in the murky air of Good Friday afternoon, April 7, A.D. 30.

Strange things happened then. The earth trembled and rocks crashed from the hillsides. Graves burst open. And the veil that hid the altar in the Temple was ripped from top to bottom, although no man's hand had touched it.

Those at the cross who loved Him beat their breasts and sobbed. And the Roman officer who had given the orders for His execution fell on his knees and gasped:

"Indeed this Man *was* the Son of God."

The Resurrection

THEY buried Jesus that same afternoon.

Mary, His mother, and Mary Cleophas, her sister, and Mary Magdalen, and John, and the two good judges of the Sanhedrin who had voted to free Jesus—Nicodemus and Joseph of Arimathea—were there. They buried Him in a tomb in the garden of Joseph of Arimathea's house, a tomb the judge had built for the day of his own death.

While the women wept, and prayed, the men laid Jesus in the grave. And they sealed the opening of that tomb with a giant white boulder, rolling it into place, firmly closing the tomb. They thought they had closed it forever.

Then, silent, and aching-hearted they went to the upper room, the room where only twenty-four hours before Jesus had shared the Last Supper with His apostles.

They were all there that Friday night—all except Judas. They sat around the oaken table wordlessly staring at the stone walls and the high-beamed ceiling, remembering.

They remembered every moment of the three years they had spent with Him. The way He had called them to follow Him. The first miracle, the wine at the wedding feast in Cana. The woman at the well in Samaria, and Jacob, the rich man's son who was healed. The Sermon on the Mount, those blessed words. The little daughter of Jairus, and the boy, Seth, with the loaves and fishes. The hour of glory when the Master was transfigured, and the night He walked on the stormy sea. And the day He called Lazarus back from the dead. . . .

Miracles, and the words of truth floated through their minds, the uncounted healings of His hands, the infinite power of love in His eyes.

And remembering, they wept.

Why should it end this way? they whispered. What are we to do now? We are afraid to go out, afraid we too will be arrested. And Jesus is dead. We have no leader. No one to serve. It is over. Finished!

The apostles sat in the rain-lashed darkness of that night, lonely, fearful, and discouraged, more than men have ever been since.

Jesus was dead. They could think no further than that. They could not seem to remember the promise He had made to them, so often, so clearly.

He had told them He would die—yes! But He had told them more than that, had told them the greatest, most beautiful secret of all time. How *could* they forget?

Through the darkness of Friday night, and through Saturday and that night too, they stayed in the upper room. This was the Jewish Sabbath, the day when no one could work, or journey far distances, the day to be kept holy for the Lord. But it was not simply because of the Sabbath that they stayed. They were afraid.

Only Mary, His mother, seemed undisturbed. Apart from the others, she prayed day and night and her face was calm.

But the apostles, disconsolate, forlorn—they were a sorry lot.

Meanwhile, in those bleak hours, others were busy in Jerusalem. From the castle of Pontius Pilate soldiers marched, out to the garden of Joseph of Arimathea, out to the sealed tomb.

Caiphas had come to Pilate, Caiphas who remembered though the apostles had forgotten.

"Sire," said High Priest Caiphas to Pilate, "we have remembered that Jesus said while He was still alive: 'After three days, I will rise again.' Will you, therefore, command that His tomb be guarded till the third day—just to be certain this can never happen?"

And Pilate had sent Roman soldiers to the grave, had them test the firmness of the stone, and commanded them to guard the tomb with their lives.

Through the dark watches of Holy Saturday night, eleven men from Galilee, apostles without a Master, and four faithful women, prayed and wondered and wept.

But just before dawn, one person left that room, a woman who loved her Lord, Mary Magdalen. She wrapped her veil and mantle close to her and stepped noiselessly out the door, and sped on tiptoe through the city.

She was the first to reach the tomb.

Breathless she entered Joseph of Arimathea's garden. And what she saw there in the dim light filled her with dread.

The stone had been rolled away. And the tomb—was empty!

Easter morning had dawned at last.

Jesus was risen, risen from the dead. He had died and death could not hold Him. He had triumphed over death, resurrected He was, risen and shining.

The first Easter—a morning of wonder and of glory, of angels gleaming on the rolled-back stone proclaiming the message:

"He is not here! Christ the Lord is risen!"

And Mary Magdalen, alone in the garden, saw Jesus and talked with Him, saw Him all alive, and smiling, with

glory round His face and form, and tenderness in His voice.

Soon all were to see Him, and talk with Him, to eat with Him even, and know Him for their own. Thomas, doubting Thomas, would feel the wounds in Jesus' hands, and be convinced that this indeed was the same Jesus Who had died on the cross.

Forty days He would spend with them in Galilee, forty days of blessing, and final preparation. Then from the Mount of Olives, before their eyes He would ascend into heaven, vanishing into the silver shelter of a cloud.

Soon too, the Holy Ghost would come upon these first Christians in tongues of fire on Pentecost, and then they would go forth into the whole world, as Jesus had commanded, teaching all nations. And the men and women whom they taught, would teach others, and the truth would pass through the years unchanged. From those same apostles to you and to me would come the greatest story ever told, about the greatest life ever lived—the story of Jesus Christ.

But all that was still in the future that first Easter Sunday morning.

Then the apostles knew only one thing: the stone was rolled back. The tomb was empty. And Jesus, Son of Man, Son of God, was risen, returned from the dead.

The words of the angels on that morning of sunburst echoed in their hearts, the never-to-be-forgotten answer to the blackness of Good Friday:

"Christ is risen!"